ELECTRICITY

and

RELATED REGULATIONS

A *Handbook for Compliance*

Revised Third Edition

Trevor E. Marks
ARTCS, CEng, MIEE, MInstMC, FInstD

RADIKAL PHASE
Unit 6, Willow Court, Cordy Lane,
Underwood, Nottingham NG16 5FD.
Tel: 01773 764 288. Fax: 01773 764 282

© **William Ernest Publishing Limited** 1991, 1994, 2002

First Edition published 1991
     Reprinted 1991, 1992

Second Edition published 1994
Third Edition published 2002

Published by William Ernest Publishing Limited

British Library Cataloguing in Publication Data

Marks, Trevor E.
   Electricity at Work and Related Regulations:
   Handbook for Compliance.
   - 3 Rev. ed
   I. Title
   621 . 31924

   ISBN 1 - 904126 - 03 - 0

Printed in England by Phase - Nottingham Tel: 01773 764 288

Preface

There have been a number of changes in British Standards since this book was first published and there has been a large quantity of legislation introduced which works with and relates to the Electricity at Work Regulations; it was therefore felt that the book should be revised. Due to the book being so widely known it was decided to keep the name of this book the same and has now been completely revised for the third time. This now reflects the latest legislation and provides a much wider scope than previous editions.

Previous changes have been maintained for continuity and ease of use such as all the regulations being put in to italics so that they stand out from the rest of the text and to repeat them in various chapters to reduce the amount the reader has to refer back to a previous chapter. Having the regulations in italics also means that the reader who can remember a regulation can easily skip reading that regulation again and just carry on reading the general text.

The book includes chapters on; earthing and equipotential bonding, automatic disconnection, and portable equipment. The chapter three on Relationship with other legislation has been further expanded. Chapter twelve Inspection and Testing has been revised to reflect the periods of inspection in more detail. . The chapter on portable equipment includes details of who can carry out the maintenance, lists the inspections and tests to be carried out, and includes a table suggesting the frequency of inspections and tests. The chapter also includes a maintenance schedule and information on the inspection and testing of business equipment such as, computers.

The book can be used by engineers as an aide mémoire and will help electricians, contractors, safety officers, works engineers and all those who are responsible for controlling personnel using electricity at work. Teachers and lecturers will find the book useful and it will also help those who are in charge of premises who have little or no knowledge of electrical matters, by giving them details of the requirements of the various regulations, enabling them to formulate instructions to give to outside parties for the checking of their electrical system and equipment. It will also assist those who wish to undertake the inspection and testing of their own portable appliances.

Kevin W. Marks 2002

Notation used for different regulations

Since the various regulations are all numbered the same way, the following abbreviations have been used so that the reader can readily recognise the type of legislation the regulation number is from.

HSW (HSW Act)	The Health and Safety at work etc. Act 1974.
EAW (EAWR)	Electricity at Work Regulations 1989.
PUWE (PUWER)	Provision and Use of Work Equipment Regulations 1992
WHSW (WHSWR)	Workplace (Health, Safety and Welfare) Regulations 1992
MHSW (MHSWR)	Management of Health and Safety at Work Regulations 1992
SM (SMR)	The Supply of Machinery (Safety) Regulations 1992

Acknowledgements

Extracts from the IEC Standards have been used with the permission of the International Electrotechnical Commission, which retains the copyright.

Extracts from legislation and the Improvement and Prohibition Notices have been made with permission of the Controller of HMSO.

Extracts from British Standards are quoted by kind permission of the British Standards Institution.

Extracts from BS 7671 the IEE Wiring Regulations etc., are quoted by kind permission of the Institution of Electrical Engineers.

Metrotest Instruments for providing the illustrations of their prospective short-circuit tester (PSC), residual current device tester (RCD), portable appliance tester (PAT), fusible leads and their 8-in-1 test station that conforms fully to all the requirements of the 16th Edition Wiring Regulations BS 7671.

Avo International Ltd. for providing the photograph of the Megger Earth Tester used for testing the resistance of earth electrodes etc.

Seton Ltd. for providing the photographs of the interlocking tabs from their Safety and Identification products mail order catalogue.

Addresses for the above will be found in the appendices.

Finally, thanks go to all those people that helped with not just this revision but with the previous and first drafts, and for the helpful suggestions they have made, even though they wish to remain anonymous. They at least will know who who they are.

Contents

Chapter 1

Introduction

Concern for electrical safety started towards the end of the last century, the first Rules and Regulations being issued by the Society of Telegraph Engineers and of Electricians on the 21st June 1882, this society later becoming the Institution of Electrical Engineers.

The Home Office, which had responsibility for industrial safety, set up a departmental committee to report on miscellaneous dangerous trades. This committee reported on the conditions of working in Electrical Generating Works in 1897, which were on the increase due to the demand for electricity in factories. A joint select committee of the House of Lords and House of Commons on Electrical Energy (Generating Stations and Supply) made recommendations for safety in 1898. But it was not until the 1901 Factories and Workshop Act enabled the Secretary of State to make regulations for dangerous trades, that the Chief Inspector of factories was asked to appoint an electrical engineer to propose regulations for the generation and use of electricity; which led to the Electricity Regulations of 1908 being drafted by Gilbert Scott Ram, who was the first Electrical Inspector of Factories.

It is to the credit of Gilbert Scott Ram that with sensible enforcement they have remained substantially unchanged since 1908, with only minor modifications being required after they were extended in 1944 to cover the 1937 Factories Act, which superseded the 1901 Act to cover other kinds of work not previously covered by Statutes. The regulations then became known throughout industry as the Electricity (Factories Act) Special Regulations of 1908 and 1944.

In the 94 years since the 1908 regulations came into force there have been many advances in electrical technology and the use of electricity has spread into many environments other than factories. In 1970 a Committee on Health and Safety at Work was set up under the chairmanship of Lord Robens, which in 1972 produced the 'Robens Report'. This report recommended the replacement piecemeal of outdated legislation, and specifically identified electricity as a target for new regulations applicable to all work places.

Draft regulations were made a few years ago and after consultations and modifications resulted in the Electricity at Work Regulations of 1989; these regulations being made under the Health and Safety at Work etc. Act of 1974 and were laid before Parliament on the 24th April 1989, by placing them on the table in the House of Commons; having rested on the table in the House for the requisite period they automatically became law.

The EAW Regulations came into force on the 1st April 1990 and it has been estimated that they will now offer protection to some 20 million people whereas the previous regulations only protected some six million.

The regulations have been written so that they give the principles of electrical safety so that technological change and the changes in the way work is carried out will not affect the regulations. It also means that they will be compatible with EEC directives and will not be affected by the 1992 Single Community Act. However, other legislation has now come into force which is related to the Electricity at Work Regulations.

Where the EAW Regulations are applicable

They cover all places where work is carried out using electricity, which includes such premises as Universities, Colleges, Hospitals, Research Centres, Construction Sites, Jobbing Sites, Commercial Premises, Factories, Generating Stations, Electricity Supplier's Networks to name but a few. They are not applicable to domestic premises but would cover work being carried out by a contractor on domestic premises, they also cover mines and quarries, but this book will not be covering the additional regulations set out in part III of the regulations, which are just for mines.

What the EAW Regulations cover

They cover all electrical equipment, which includes switchgear, control panels, distribution boards, electrical accessories, portable tools and equipment and cables and apply to all electrical systems including portable generators, batteries, battery operated torches and instruments containing a source of electricity.

The date the existing electrical equipment or electrical installation was ordered, or the standards it was manufactured or installed to, or the date it was put into use, is immaterial, the regulations apply to all such equippment. Such installations or electrical equipment do not have to be changed unless they are likely to cause danger by becoming unsafe.

EEC Directives and other changes

EEC Directives have caused a considerable amount of new legislation to be introduced in the U.K. after the EAW Regulations became law. This legislation does not affect the EAW Regulations but adds to the requirements to be taken into account. The additional regulations being covered in this third edition of the book.

The IEE 15th Edition Wiring Regulations was superseded by the 16th Edition of those regulations on the 1st January 1993. The IEE Wiring Regulations were also made into British Standard 7671 at the end of 1992. BS 7671: 2001 is the national standard for electrical installation work at the time this third edition is being prepared

Other changes were caused by new British Standards and changes to existing ones.

Chapter 2

Electrical terminology explained

Before delving into the EAW Regulations in detail it is wise to consider the terminology since this will enable a better understanding of the regulations. Some of the definitions are very wide in their scope which is not obvious when they are skipped through; comments have therefore been made where appropriate after the definition. Other definitions have been included after the EAW Regulations definitions so that non-electrical people can understand the electrical terminology.

Conductor

The definition is: *a conductor of electrical energy.* This means any material that will conduct electricity in its solid, liquid or gaseous state; glass is an insulator in its solid state but will conduct electricity in its liquid state, so in its liquid state the regulations applicable to conductors apply to glass. It is the same for any other material which in one particular state is an insulator but which will conduct electricity in either or both of the other states. The definition includes such items as the electrolyte in a plating bath, the gas in a fluorescent tube, steel structures and the metal casing round electrical equipment. (See Figure 2.1.)

Circuit conductor

A circuit conductor *means any conductor in a system which is intended to carry electric current in normal conditions, or to be energised in normal conditions and includes a combined neutral and earth conductor* but does not include a conductor provided solely to perform a protective function by connection to earth or other reference point.* See Figure 2.1. (*See later definition.)

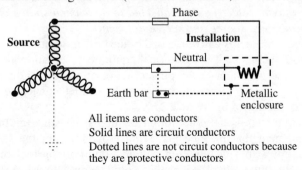

Figure 2.1 - Illustrating conductors and circuit conductors

Electrical Equipment

Includes anything used, intended to be used or installed for use,

to generate,	a.c. or d.c. generation
provide,	electrical energy
transmit,	overhead lines, underground cables, radio, T.V., telephone
transform,	change voltage or frequency
rectify,	change from a.c to d.c or d.c to a.c.
convert,	both static and rotary
conduct,	liquids, solids, gases
distribute,	fibre optic, data transmission, telephone, television cables, HV and LV cables etc.
control,	standard, logic, radio
store,	batteries, capacitors
measure	instrumentation, test instruments, portable instruments
or use electrical	
energy	fixed equipment, portable equipment, computers, typewriters etc.

This definition includes all equipment and conductors irrespective of the voltage for example, a battery powered torch is included. It includes the power station and all equipment, cables etc., from the power station to the final lighting point or socket outlet. Note that the definition includes the words 'intended to be used', which means that the scope of the definition is almost unlimited.

A circuit which has been isolated is still within the scope of the definition since it is intended to be used at some time. Installed for use does not mean you are using it; a socket outlet may not be used, but it is installed for use. Electrical materials can be at any voltage and used in all sorts of locations.

System

System in a regulation *means an electrical system in which all the electrical equipment is, or may be, electrically connected to a common source of electrical energy, and includes such source and such equipment.*

A source of electrical energy can be a.c. or d.c. and be from a battery or a generator. A system therefore includes all the electrical equipment, circuit conductors and conductors from the generator at the power station to the last lighting point or portable appliance or tool connected to a socket outlet connected to a final distribution board. As shown in Figure 2.2.

The most important words in this definition are 'or may be' since this brings items of electrical equipment that may be just lying around within the scope of the definition and thereby within the scope of the regulations. Portable tools and portable equipment fall within this category since they could be put into use at any time.

This definition is also linked to the definition of electrical equipment and conductors, consequentially items of non-electrical services that are connected to the main earth bar of the electrical installation become part of the system.

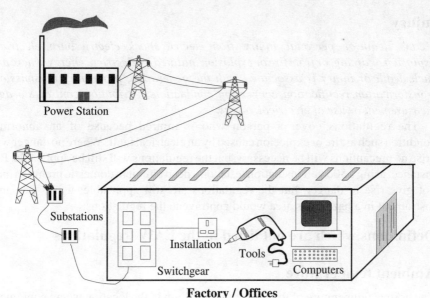

Figure 2.2 - System

The impact of this definition also means that items that have been isolated or disconnected are still part of the system since they may be used. Unless the circuit has been dismantled and identified, so as not to be connected, it is still part of the system.

Systems can be inside, outside, below ground, or above ground; they can be old, new or on a construction site.

A test instrument becomes part of the system when it is connected to it for testing purposes. Where an instrument contains a source of electrical energy either a generator or batteries it can itself form a system. Electrical circuits can be isolated from the normal power supply to enable tests to be carried out. Such circuits will then become part of the system formed by the test instrument containing a source of electrical energy and brings such circuits and electrical equipment within the scope of the regulations. This is important in hazardous areas.

A transformer does not insert a break in the system, although there is no electrical connection between the primary and the secondary windings, electrical energy is transmitted through the transformer.

Danger

Means risk of injury. Some regulations mention *preventing danger*; to prevent danger therefore means prevent the risk of injury.

Injury

Means death or personal injury from electric shock, electric burn, electrical explosion or arcing, or from fire or explosion initiated by electrical energy, where any such death or injury is associated with the generation, provision, transmission, transformation, rectification, conversion, conduction, distribution, control, storage, measurement or use of electrical energy.

The regulations cover a person who is injured because of an abnormal condition such as fire or explosion caused by an electrical fault. Where no danger will arise no precautions will be necessary, but the regulations will still be applicable. For instance, using a 500 volt insulation tester on a dead circuit in domestic premises may not give rise to danger, but the regulations are still applicable; using the same instrument in a hazardous area would contravene the regulations.

Definitions which are not listed in the EAW Regulations

Ambient temperature

The normal temperature of the air or other medium in the location where equipment is to be used.

Arm's reach

The limit to which a person can reach within a zone of accessibility without assistance, as outlined in Figure 2.3.

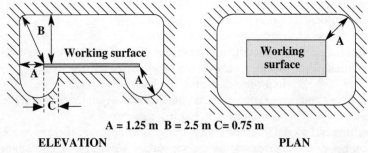

A = 1.25 m B = 2.5 m C= 0.75 m

ELEVATION   PLAN

Figure 2.3 - Arm's Reach

Automatic disconnection

The protective device (i.e. fuse, circuit breaker or residual current device) operates automatically when a fault occurs in the circuit it protects.

Breaking capacity

A value of fault current that a protective device is capable of breaking under defined conditions without danger arising.

Charged

Means it is either live or has become charged with a voltage, by for instance static electricity, capacitance, or induced voltage.

Circuit protective conductor

A conductor connecting the metallic enclosure round electrical equipment (exposed-conductive-parts) to the main earthing terminal.

Current-carrying capacity

The maximum current equipment or conductor can carry without exceeding the permissible operating temperature of the equipment or cable, with a given ambient temperature.

Dead

Dead means that there is no potential on the equipment concerned, i.e. it is neither live nor charged.

Direct contact

Contact with normally energised phase or neutral parts that may result in electric shock.

Earth fault loop impedance

The impedance or resistance of the phase conductor and protective conductor from the source of energy to the point of a phase to earth fault or, to the point of measuring the phase earth loop impedance, as illustrated in Figure 2.4.

Energy let-through

The total energy let-through a protective device before the device finally interrupts the fault current flowing in the circuit concerned.

Equipotential bonding

An electrical connection between exposed-conductive-parts and extraneous-conductive-parts which puts them approximately at the same potential.

In Figure 2.5, a fault to earth in the switch raises the voltage on the metalwork (exposed-conductive-parts), but because of the cable connection to the radiator pipe work (extraneous-conductive-part), approximately the same voltage appears on the radiator, thus there is no significant voltage difference between the switch and the radiator. Although there could be a significant difference with other conductive parts.

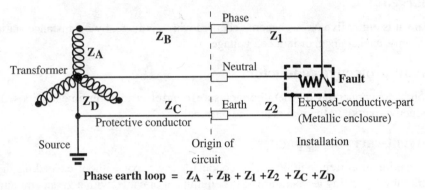

Phase earth loop $= Z_A + Z_B + Z_1 + Z_2 + Z_C + Z_D$

Figure 2.4 - Phase earth loop impedance

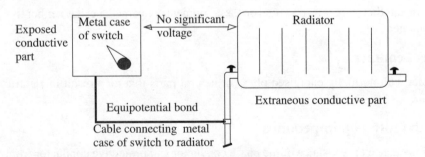

Figure 2.5 - Equipotential (supplementary) bonding

Exposed-conductive-part

Metalwork of electrical equipment which can be touched and which is not a live part but may become live under fault conditions.

Extraneous-conductive-part

Metalwork that is not part of the electrical installation, which is liable to introduce a potential, generally earth potential.

Extra-low voltage

A voltage not exceeding 50V a.c. or 120V ripple free d.c between conductors, or any conductor and earth.

Rectified a.c. invariably has an a.c. voltage superimposed onto the d.c voltage giving a ripple voltage. For a 120V ripple free d.c. system the maximum peak value allowed is either 128.5V or 140V, as illustrated in Figure 2.6.

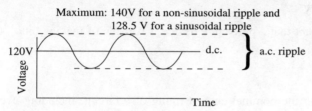

Figure 2.6 - Ripple created by rectified a.c.

Impedance 'Z'

The total virtual resistance of an electrical circuit to alternating current, arising from the resistance and resultant reactance 'X' of the conductor (X_L -X_C). The impedance Z being obtained as shown in Figure 2.7.

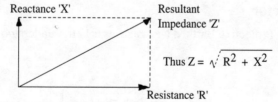

$$Z = \sqrt{R^2 + X^2}$$

Figure 2.7 - Impedance triangle

Indirect contact

Contact of persons or livestock with exposed-conductive-parts made live by a fault and which may result in electric shock.

Live

Live means that the item is at a potential i.e. it has a voltage on it as in normal use with respect to other conductive parts. Note that neutrals are considered to be live conductors.

Live part

A phase or neutral conductor or part of equipment intended to be energised in normal use.

Low voltage

A voltage exceeding 50V a.c. but not exceeding 1000V a.c. between conductors or 600V a.c between any conductor and earth.

A voltage exceeding 120V d.c. but not exceeding 1500V d.c between conductors, or 900V d.c. between any conductor and earth.

Making capacity

The peak fault current that a protective device is capable of making onto, under defined conditions.

Overcurrent

A current exceeding the nominal current rating of a circuit, including overload current and fault current. The nominal current rating of conductors is their current-carrying capacity.

Overload current

A current exceeding the nominal current rating of an electrically sound circuit or equipment.

PEN conductor

PEN stands for Protective Earthed Neutral, this is better understood by considering Figure 2.8.

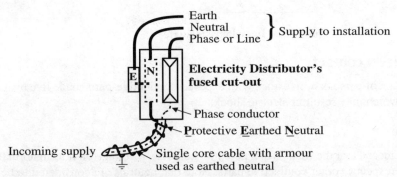

Figure 2.8 - PEN conductor

Figure 2.8 shows the Electricity Distributor's Cut-Out as provided for a single phase supply. The incoming supply is an armoured single core cable, the inner core being the phase conductor, sometimes referred to as the line conductor, which is connected to the fuse in the Cut-Out. The armour is connected to the neutral block in the Cut-Out, which in turn is connected to an earth terminal on the outside of the case. The armour is therefore used as the neutral conductor and the earth for the installation and is known as a Protective Earthed Neutral i.e. PEN conductor. It is therefore designed to carry current in normal use, i.e. the neutral current, and is therefore a circuit conductor as far as the regulations are concerned. The earth conductor connected to the earth terminal on the outside of the Cut-Out is not designed to carry current in normal use and is therefore only a conductor as far as the regulations are concerned.

Protective conductor

A conductor used as part of a measure for the protection against electric shock by connecting extraneous-conductive-parts together, or to exposed-conductive-parts, or connecting any exposed-or extraneous-conductive-parts to the main earth terminal.

Protective device

In the text of the handbook, it is a device installed in a circuit to protect the circuit by disconnecting the supply to it if there is an overload, short circuit, or a phase to earth fault.

Residual current device

A current-operated earth-leakage circuit breaker. Abbreviated to RCD. One type of RCD is an RCCB, - residual current circuit breaker.
(Operation explained in Chapter 7.)

Short-circuit current

A current caused by a fault of negligible impedance (resistance) between phase conductors or phase and neutral conductors.

Simultaneously accessible

Equipment or parts which can be touched at the same time by a person or, where applicable, by livestock.

Withstand capacity

The maximum current that a device can withstand flowing through it without being damaged or causing a danger to arise.

Chapter 3

Relationship with other legislation

The Electricity at Work Regulations have been made under the Health and Safety at Work etc. Act 1974 (HSW Act) and as such can be regarded as an extension of that Act. The HSW Act places general duties on all people at work. There is, however, other legislation that has also to be taken into account when considering the Electricity at Work Regulations 1989. These comprise the Management of Health and Safety at Work Regulations 1992, the Provision and Use of Work Equipment Regulations 1998 and the Personal Protective Equipment at Work Regulations 1992.

The Health and Safety at Work Act is the legislation which also protects the general public who are not at work from the actions of those at work, as outlined in Section 1 of Part 1 of Chapter 37.

Part 1 of the HSW Act

Section 1 of the HSW Act details the objectives of Part 1. These are mainly concerned with securing the health, safety and welfare of people at work and with protecting other people from risks caused by the way in which work activities are conducted. So the HSW Act covers the general public as well as people at work as outlined in Section 3 of the Act.

If lighting was installed on scaffolding round a building and due to a fault the general public received an electric shock, the installer could be prosecuted under the HSW Act as well as the EAW Regulations.

The HSW Act imposes duties on employers, the self-employed, employees, manufacturers, suppliers, designers, importers and persons in control of premises.

The HSW Act is an enabling act written in general terms, but it enables more specific legislation to be made where this is appropriate. The aim is for new regulations to be supported by Approved Codes of Practice (ACOP) supplemented by Guidance Notes. This is done to assist people to understand the law and point out what needs to be done in practice to comply with it. This is what has happened in the case of the Electricity at Work Regulations, which revoke the following statutory provisions:

The Electricity Regulations 1908

The Electricity (Factories Act) Special Regulations 1944

Regulation 12 The Manufacture of Cinematograph Film Regulations 1928

Regulation 14 The Cinematograph Film Stripping Regulations 1939

Regulation 44 The Construction (General Provisions) Regulations 1961

Regulation 3(2) (a) The Factories Act 1961 etc. (Repeals and Modification Regulations 1974

Various Mines and Quarries Regulations.

Not all regulations have been revoked, there are other regulations still in force that need to be complied with. The following regulations are still in force:

The Electricity Supply Regulations 1988 (as amended) (Soon to be replaced by

TheElectricity Safety and Continuity Regulations 2002).

The Low Voltage Electrical Equipment (Safety) Regulations 1989

The Cinematographic (Safety) Regulations 1955

The Building Standards (Scotland) Regulations 1981

Regulation 27(1) of The Electricity Supply Regulations 1989 is concerned with the electrical installation in consumers' premises, but Regulation 27(2) states that where the installation complies with the provisions of the IEE Wiring Regulations (now BS 7671) it shall be deemed to comply with the requirements of Regulation 27(1) as to safety.

The Low Voltage Electrical Equipment (Safety) Regulations 1989 are applicable to all Low Voltage electrical equipment, with the exception of equipment for use in: an explosive atmosphere, radiology and medical purposes, parts for goods lifts, electricity supply meters, plugs, socket outlets and adaptors for domestic use, fence controllers and specialised electrical equipment for use on ships, aircraft or railways, which comply with safety provisions drawn up by international bodies.

Where electrical installations are carried out in accordance with BS 7671 IEE Wiring Regulations they are deemed to comply with the Scottish Building Regulations.

Types of Regulation

There are two types of EAW Regulation; those imposing absolute duties and those imposing a 'so far as is reasonably practicable' standard. Regulations that do not contain the clause 'so far as is reasonably practicable' are deemed to be absolute, the regulations can therefore be broken down into two groups as shown in Figure 3.1, i.e. absolute regulations and 'so far as is reasonably practicable' regulations.

Where the requirement of a regulation is absolute it must be applied regardless of the expense or any other reason. The conditions of the regulations have to be met irrespective of the size of the company or organisation. The excuse that a company or person could not afford to comply with the regulation is not an acceptable defence.

All duties under the Electricity at Work Regulations are limited by the phrase 'to matters which are within his control', from EAW Regulation 3 (1)(a).

Absolute Regulations	Defence Regulation 29 applicable	Regulations 'so far as is reasonably practicable'
4(4)	4(4)	4(1), 4(2), 4(3)
5	5	6
8	8	7
9	9	12(3)
10	10	
11	11	
12(1), 12(2)	12	
13	13	
14	14	
15	15	
16	16	

Figure 3.1 - Absolute and 'so far as is reasonably practicable' Regulations

The EAW Regulations also provide Regulation 29 that can be used as a defence for a contravention of an absolute regulation if criminal proceedings are taken against the duty holder. EAW **Regulation 29** states:

'In any proceedings for an offence consisting of a contravention of regulations 4(4), 5, 8, 9, 10,11, 12, 13, 14, 15, 16 or 25, (i.e., absolute regulations) it shall be a defence for any person to prove that he took all reasonable steps and exercised all due diligence to avoid the commission of that offence.'

This means that the accused has to prove that he was careful and rigorous in determining the dangers that may occur and took appropriate steps to avoid those dangers. It should be noted that, whereas the burden of proof usually lies with the prosecution, in this case the defendant must prove that he has done everything he possibly could to comply with the regulation.

It should also be noted that this defence only becomes relevant once it has been established that an offence has been committed. It should not be a consideration that affects the judgement of the duty holder when he is deciding what steps to take to meet an absolute requirement.

When considering the regulations containing the clause 'so far as is reasonably practicable' consideration has to be given to Section 40 of the HSW Act.

Section 40 HSW Act. 'In any proceedings for an offence under any of the relevant statutory provisions consisting of a failure to comply with a duty or requirement to do something so far as is practicable or to use the best practicable means to do something, it shall be for the accused to prove (as the case may be) that it was not practicable or not reasonably practicable to do more than was in fact done to satisfy the duty or requirement, or that there was no better practicable means than was in fact used to satisfy the duty or requirement.'

Again the burden of proof is on the accused to prove that the precautions taken were good enough. The Courts have already interpreted what is meant by 'so far as is reasonably practicable' as requiring an assessment to be made on the one hand of the gravity of the risk and on the other hand, the physical difficulties, time, trouble and expense which would be involved in taking steps to avert the risk. If for instance, the risks of injury are very low and the cost or technical difficulties of taking steps to eliminate those slight risks are very high, it might not be judged 'reasonably practicable' to take those steps.

The greater the risks the less reason there is for not taking protective measures to avoid injury. This means that the greater the risk the more the reasonably practicable requirements approach absolute requirements.

A precaution that is reasonably practicable for a prosperous company, employer, or self-employed person, is equally reasonably practicable for the less well off. What is important to note from Section 40 of the HSW Act, is that it is for the accused to prove it was not reasonably practicable to do more than he did.

Approved codes of practice

Note should also be taken of Section 17 of the HSW Act which concerns the use of Approved Codes of Practice (ACOP) in criminal proceedings. An outline of Section 17(2) is given below:

'Any provision of the code of practice which appears to the court to be relevant to the requirement or prohibition alleged to have been contravened shall be admissible in evidence in the proceedings; and if it is proved that there was at any material time a failure to observe any provision of the code which appears to the court is relevant to the proceedings, that matter shall be taken as proved, unless the court is satisfied that the requirement or prohibition alleged to have been committed was complied with otherwise than by way of observance of that provision of the code.'

This means that in order to get a conviction the prosecution only have to prove the Approved Code of Practice is relevant to the offence with which the accused is charged and that it was not followed. The defendant will then be convicted unless he can convince the Court that what he did was just as good as the Approved Code of Practice which might be difficult in such circumstances.

It can be seen from the above that the approved code is the accepted standard. Approved codes can be those issued by the Health and Safety Executive or any other codes or standards that are formally approved by the Health and Safety Commission under Section 16 of the HSW Act. One such Approved Code is BS 697 'Rubber gloves for electrical purposes'.

Ordinary codes of practice

Not all codes are approved codes of practice. The difference between them is that the prosecution only have to prove to the Court that an approved code is relevant. With any other code they can only point out to the accused that a code of practice is in existence and ask why the accused did not comply with that code.

Training

The employer, whether a company, partnership or a self-employed person must provide for any employees such information, instruction, training and supervision as is necessary to ensure their health and safety at work. Provision of training is specified by Section 2(2)(c) of the HSW Act and by Regulation 11 of the Management of Health and Safety at Work Regulations 1992, this latter legislation also requires the employer to take into account a person's competence before entrusting any tasks to him.

Regulation 11 (MHSWR) : Capabilities and training

(1) Every employer shall, in entrusting tasks to his employees, take into account their capabilities as regards health and safety.

(2) Every employer shall ensure that his employees are provided with adequate health and safety training -

(a) on their being recruited into the employer's undertaking; and

(b) on their being exposed to new or increased risks because of -

    (i) their being transferred or given a change of responsibilities within the employer's undertaking,

    Clauses (ii), (iii), (iv) and (iv) then cover the introduction of new equipment, or a change of work equipment, introduction of new technology, a change in the system of working or a new system of work .... etc.

Item 3 of the MHSW Regulations specifies that the training referred to has to be repeated periodically, where appropriate, and adapted to take into account any new or changed risks; it must also take place during working hours.

Regulations 9 of the Provision and Use of Work Equipment Regulations 1998 (PUWER) also specifies that persons who use work equipment must receive adequate training in the methods adopted when using the work equipment and in the risks that may be entailed in using such equipment. For example, an electrician should have received training in the use of test equipment and in the dangers of using such equipment; this would include the danger of using a multi-meter, with voltage and current ranges, where a voltage test could be made with the selector switch set on the wrong (e.g. current) range. It is also a requirement of <u>PUWE Regulation 9</u> that employees supervising and managing the work equipment must also receive instruction and training.

Regulation 9 *(PUWER):* **Training**

   (1) Every employer shall ensure that all persons who use work equipment have received adequate training for purposes of health and safety, including training in the methods which may be adopted when using the work equipment, any risks which such use may entail and precautions to be taken.

   (2) Every employer shall ensure that any of his employees who supervises or manages the use of work equipment has received adequate training for purposes of health and safety, including training in the methods which may be adopted when using the work equipment, any risks which such use may entail and precautions to be taken.

The employer should therefore make arrangements to make employees aware of the requirements of the Electricity at Work Regulations and any Approved Codes of Practice applicable to the type of installation they operate. The employees should also have access to a copy of the Regulations and any Approved Codes of Practice. Additionally, the employer should also make available for reference any other codes of practice and relevant standards that are applicable to the type of work undertaken by his employees.

Design, manufacture, import or supply

The Supply of Machinery (Safety) Regulations 1992 (SM Regulations) cover all machinery provided for the processing, treatment, moving or packaging of material. Schedule 3 of these Regulations details Annex I of the Machinery Directive for the 'Essential Health and Safety Requirements Relating to the Design and Construction of Machinery' However, not all machinery is covered by these regulations.

Regulation 7 *(SMR): These Regulations do not apply to machinery first supplied or put into service in the Community before the 1st January 1993.*

Where the risk regarding safety of electrical equipment is not mainly of an electrical origin (i.e., mechanical, chemical etc.) the equipment is covered by the SM Regulations. But, the SM Regulations are not applicable for electrical equipment where the risk to safety is of an electrical origin.

In general the duties of the designer, manufacturer, supplier and the user of equipment are covered by the SM Regulations, the PUWE Regulations and Section 6 of the HSW Act. Section 6 of the HSW Act also covers equipment not covered by other legislation.

Although the Health and Safety at Work etc Act 1974 has not in itself been altered, several changes have been made to the Act of 1974 by other legislation. The most onerous amendment was made by the Consumer Protection Act 1987, which changed Section 6. Section 6 (as amended) of the HSW Act must also be considered along with the Electricity at Work Regulations and since its details are buried in other legislation it is, with the exception of those particular clauses for fairground equipment or the supply and manufacture of substances, repeated here.

Section 6(1) It shall be the duty of any person who designs, manufactures, imports or supplies any article for use at work or any article of fairground equipment-

   (a) to ensure, so far as is reasonably practicable, that the article is so designed and constructed that it will be safe and without risks to health at all times when it is being set, used, cleaned or maintained by a person at work;

   (b) to carry out or arrange for the carrying out of such testing and examination as may be necessary for the performance of the duty imposed on him by the preceding paragraph;

   (c) to take such steps as are necessary to secure that persons supplied by that person with the article are provided with adequate information about the use for which the article is designed or has been tested and about any conditions necessary to ensure that it will be safe and without risks to health at all such times as are mentioned in paragraph (a) above and when it is being dismantled or disposed of; and

   (d) to take such steps as are necessary to secure, so far as is reasonably practicable, that persons so supplied are provided with all such revisions of information provided to them by virtue of the preceding paragraph as are necessary by reason of its becoming known that anything gives rise to a serious risk to health or safety.

Section 6 (1A) Places similar duties (as given above) on any person who designs, manufacture, imports or supplies any article of fairground equipment. Clauses a, b, c, and d being similar to the same clauses of Section 6(1), the duty being to members of the public as opposed to persons at work.

Section 6(2) It shall be the duty of any person who undertakes the design or manufacture of any article for use at work or of any article of fairground equipment to carry out or arrange for the carrying out of any necessary research with a view to the discovery and, so far as is reasonably practicable, the elimination or minimisation of any risks to health or safety to which the design or article may give rise.

Section 6(3) It shall be the duty of any person who erects or installs any article for use at work in any premises where that article is to be used by persons at work or who erects or installs any article of fairground equipment to ensure, so far as is reasonably practicable, that nothing about the way in which the article is erected or installed makes it unsafe or a risk to health at any such time as is mentioned in paragraph (a) of subsection (1) or, as the case may be, in paragraph (a) of subsection (1) or (1A) above.

Section 6(4) It shall be the duty of any person who manufactures, imports or supplies any substance:

   (a) to ensure, so far as is reasonably practicable, that the substance will be safe and without risks to health at all times when it is being used, handled,

processed, stored, or transported by a person at work or in premises to which Section 4 * above applies. (*Premises covered by Section 4 HSW Act.)

(b)   covers the testing and examination to ensure performance of duty imposed by (a)

(c)   concerns provision of information on substances similar to Section 6(1)

(d)   concerns providing information on revisions for (c) similar to Section 6(1).

Comparing Section 6, as amended by the <u>Consumer Protection Act,</u> with the original Section 6, which is still given in the HSW Act Publication, will show how much it has been changed. Unfortunately the changes have not made it any easier to understand.

Section 6 applies to new and second-hand articles designed for use at work, whether for sale or hire. It also covers items that are designed for domestic use but which can also be used at work. The provision of information includes information on reasonably foreseeable risks, including risks that may arise from disposal or dismantling of equipment. Reasonably foreseeable includes such items as operator error or inattention.

Making up your own switchboards or control panels falls within the requirement of Section 6, this means that to comply with Section 6(2) the research called for is to determine the frequency, maximum load, any overloads, short-circuit currents, transient over-voltage, and earth fault currents that are likely to occur, and to ensure that there is no risk of electric shock from direct contact and the risk from indirect contact is reduced to a minimum.

To comply with 6(1)(a) the equipment must be designed to take all the items discovered under 6(2) into account.

Section 6(3) is calling for the equipment to be properly installed so that the installation does not make the article installed unsafe or a risk to health. This means allowing sufficient space for maintenance to be carried out, making certain the equipment is properly earthed and that all connections to the equipment are properly and securely made, that all barriers and covers are replaced after installation and that proper commissioning and testing is carried out.

As far as the suppliers of equipment are concerned 6(1)(c) imposes a duty on them to provide adequate information about the use for which the equipment is designed and has been tested. This may take the form of specifying the British Standards or other standards the equipment complies with together with details of any test certificates for tests carried out on a specimen item of the equipment.

If the installer is not in possession of the appropriate British Standard or other standards referred to, he should specify to the manufacturer the physical, mechanical, environmental conditions and electrical requirements for the equipment, including whether the equipment requires to be continuously rated and request the manufacturer to advise as to whether their equipment is suitable for the conditions to which it will be subjected.

Section 6 (5) is concerned with research and discovery concerning substances.

Section 6 (6) *Nothing in the preceding provisions of this section shall be taken to require a person to repeat any testing, examination or research which has been carried out otherwise than by him or at his instance, in so far as it is reasonable for him to rely on the results thereof for the purposes of those provisions.*

Section 6(6) relieves the purchaser of having to carry out testing, examination or research on equipment in accordance with Section 6(2) when it has already been carried out by the manufacturer. For instance, when making up a switchboard as mentioned above, it would not be necessary to re-test each individual component supplied by a manufacturer (providing the manufacturer has already complied with Section 6(2)), but it would still be necessary to ensure that the switchboard was suitable for the short-circuit currents and overload currents etc. that may occur in service. It must also be remembered that many British Standards specify tests to be carried out on equipment, cables etc. after installation. Many manufacturers print copies of test certificates in their catalogues and give the British Standard numbers to which their products have been made. In addition, most if not all, manufacturers specify the conditions under which their products have been designed to be used. Care is therefore required when selecting equipment to ensure it is used for the purpose for which it was designed.

Section 6 (7) *Any duty imposed on any person by any of the preceding provisions of this section shall extend only to things done in the course of a trade, business or other undertaking carried on by him (whether for profit or not) and to matters within his control.*

Section 6 (7) Excludes the general public from having to comply with Section 6 when carrying out work in their own domestic property. They are not excluded when carrying out work on someone else's property even if they are not charging for the work done.

Section 6 (8) *Where a person designs, manufactures, imports or supplies an article for use at work or an article of fairground equipment and does so for or to another on the basis of a written undertaking by that other to take specified steps sufficient to ensure, so far as is reasonably practicable, that the article will be safe and without risks to health at all such times as are mentioned in paragraph (a) of subsection (1) or, as the case may be, in paragraph (a) of subsection (1) or (1A) above, the undertaking shall have the effect of relieving the first-mentioned person from the duty imposed by virtue of that paragraph to such extent as is reasonable having regard to the terms of the undertaking.*

Section 6 (8) Effectively places the duty on the purchaser, where the designer, manufacturer, importer or supplier of equipment specifies in writing that the purchaser must carry out his own testing, examination, research and discovery to ensure that it will be without risks to health at all times when it is set, used, cleaned or maintained by a person at work.

Section 6 (8A) *Nothing in subsection (7) or (8) above shall relieve any person who imports any article or substance from any duty in respect of anything which:*

(a) in the case of an article designed outside the United Kingdom, was done by and in the course of any trade, profession or other undertaking carried on by, or was within the control of, the person who designed the article; or

(b) in the case of an article or substance manufactured outside the United Kingdom, was done by and in the course of any trade, profession or other undertaking carried on by, or was within the control of, the person who manufactured the article or substance.

Section 6 (8A) Stops Section 6 (7) or (8) from being used for an article designed or manufactured outside the United Kingdom where the control is still with the person who designed or manufactured the article.

Section 6 (9) Where a person ("the ostensible supplier") supplies any article or substance to another ("the customer") under a hire-purchase agreement, conditional sale agreement or credit-sale agreement, and the ostensible supplier:

(a) carries on the business of financing the acquisition of goods by others by means of such agreements; and

(b) in the course of that business acquired his interest in the article or substance supplied to the customer as a means of financing its acquisition by the customer from a third person ("the effective supplier"),

the effective supplier and not the ostensible supplier shall be treated for the purposes of this section as supplying the article or substance to the customer, and any duty imposed by the preceding provisions of this section on suppliers shall accordingly fall on the effective supplier and not on the ostensible supplier.

Section 6 (9) makes the supplier of the article responsible for compliance with Section 6 and not the firm, company or other person providing the finance for the purchaser.

Section 6 (10) For the purposes of this section an absence of safety or a risk to health shall be disregarded in so far as the case in or in relation to which it would arise is shown to be one the occurrence of which could not reasonably be foreseen; and in determining whether any duty imposed by virtue of paragraph (a) of subsection (1), (1A) or (4) above has been performed regard shall be had to any relevant information or advice which has been provided to any person by the person by whom the article has been designed, manufactured, imported or supplied or, as the case may be, by the person by whom the substance has been manufactured, imported or supplied.

Section 6 (10) covers those situations where it can be proved that a risk to health could not possibly have been foreseen after consideration has been given to any relevant information and advice provided by the designer, manufacturer, importer or supplier of the article.

HSE
Health & Safety
Executive

Health and Safety at Work etc Act 1974, Sections 21, 23, and 24 | Serial number

Improvement notice

Inspector's full name
Name
Address
Trading as*
I,
one of Her Majesty's Inspectors of

Inspector's official designation
Being an Inspector appointed by an instrument in writing made pursuant to section 19 of the said Act and entitled to issue this notice

Official address
of
Telephone number

hereby give you notice that I am of the opinion that

Location of premise or place of activity
at

you, as an employer/a self employed person/a person wholly or partly in control of the premises/other*

are contravening/have contravened in circumstances that make it likely that the contravention will continue or be repeated* the following statutory provisions:

The reasons for my said opinion are:

and I hereby require you to remedy the said contraventions or, as the case may be, the matters occasioning them

by   (and I direct that the measures specified in the Schedule which forms part of this notice shall be taken to remedy the said contraventions or matters)*

Signature   Date
An Improvement Notice is also being served on
of
related to the matters contained in the notice

Environment and Safety Information Act 1988
This is a relevent notice for the purposes of the Environment and Safety Information Act 1988   YES / NO*
This page only will form the register entry*
Signature   Date

LP1(rev 3/92)   *See notes overleaf*   *delete as appropriate*

Notes on reverse side of Improvement Notice

1   Failure to comply with this Improvement Notice is an offence as provided by Section 33(1)(g) of the Health and Safety at Work Act 1974 and section 33(2A) of this Act renders the offender liable on summary conviction, to imprisonment for a term not exceeding 6 months, or to a fine not exceeding £20,000 or both, or, on conviction on indictment, to imprisonment for a term not exceeding 2 years, or a fine, or both.

2   An Inspector has power to withdraw an Improvement Notice or to extend the period specified in the notice before the end of the period specified in it. If you wish this to be considered you should apply to the Inspector who issued the notice, but you must do so before the end of the period given in it. Such an application is not an appeal against this notice.

3   The issue of this notice does not relieve you of any legal liability for failing to comply with any statutory provision referred to in the notice or to perform any other statutory or common law duty resting on you.

4   Your attention is drawn to the provision for appeal against this notice to an Industrial Tribunal. Details of the method of making an appeal are given below, see also Section 24 of this Act. The appeal should be sent to: The Secretary of the Tribunals, Central Office of the Industrial Tribunals, Southgate Street, Bury St. Edmunds, Suffolk IP33 2AQ. (for England and Wales) or The Secretary of the Tribunals, Central Office of the Industrial Tribunals, Saint Andrews House, 141 West Nile Street, GLASGOW G1 2RU (for Scotland only).

The appeal must be commenced by sending in writing to the Secretary of the Tribunals a notice containing the following particulars :

(a)   the name of the appellant and his address for the service of documents;

(b)   the date of the notice, or notices, appealed against and the address of the premises or place concerned;

(c)   the name and address, as shown on this notice, of the respondent;

(d)   particulars of the requirements or directions appealed against; and

(e)   the grounds of the appeal.
A form which may be used for appeal is attached.

Time limit for appeal
A notice of appeal must be sent to the Secretary of Tribunals within 21 days from the date of service on the appellant of the notice, or notices, appealed against, or within such further period as the tribunal considers reasonable in a case where it is satisfied that it was not reasonably practicable for the notice of appeal to be presented within the period of 21 days. If posted the appeal should be sent by recorded delivery.

The entering of an appeal suspends the Improvement Notice until the appeal has been determined, but does not automatically alter the date given in this notice by which the matters contained in it must be remedied.

The rules for the hearing of an appeal are given in The Industrial Tribunals (Improvement and Prohibition Notices Appeals) Regulations 1974 (SI 1974 No. 1925) for England and Wales and The Industrial Tribunals (Improvement and Prohibition Notices Appeals) (Scotland) Regulations 1974 (SI 1974 No. 1926) for Scotland.

ENVIRONMENT AND SAFETY INFORMATION ACT 1988
1   A notice which is relevant for the purposes of this Act (see overleaf) will be included as an entry in a public register which will be kept by the Health and Safety Executive. A relevant notice is one which does not impose requirements or prohibitions solely for the protection of persons at work.

2   The register entry shall be made within 14 days of either the right of appeal against the notice expiring, or of such an appeal being disposed of. Where a notice is cancelled on appeal no entry shall be made.

Notes 3 to 7 have been omitted from this copy

Health and Safety at Work etc Act 1974, Sections 22, 23, and 24

Serial Number
P

Prohibition notice

Name
Address
Trading as*

Inspector's full name
I
one of Her Majesty's Inspectors of
Being an Inspector appointed by an instrument in writing made pursuant to section 19 of the said Act and entitled

Inspector's official designation
to issue the notice

Official address
of   Telephone number
hereby give you notice that I am of the opinion that the following activities namely

Location of premises or place of activity
which are being carried on by you / likely to be carried on by you / under your control* at

involve, or will involve, a risk of serious personal injury, and that the matters which give rise / will give rise* to the said risks are:

and that the said matters involve / will involve* contravention of the following statutory provisions :

because

and I hereby direct that the said activities shall not be carried on by you or under your control immediately / after* unless the said contraventions* and matters have been remedied
I further direct that the measures specified in the schedule which forms part of this notice shall be taken to remedy the said contraventions or matters*

Signature   Date

*A Prohibition Notice is also being served on
of
related to the matters contained in this notice

Environment and Safety Information Act 1988
This is a relevant notice for the purposes of the Environment and Safety Information Act 1988   YES / NO*
This page only will form the register entry*

Signature   Date

LP 2 (02. 93)   See notes overleaf   *delete as appropriate

Notes on reverse side of Prohibition Notice

1 Failure to comply with this Prohibition Notice is an offence as provided by Section 33(1)(g) of the Health and Safety at Work etc Act 1974 and section 33(2A) of this Act renders the offender liable on summary conviction, to imprisonment for a term not exceeding 6 months, or to a fine not exceeding £20,000, or both, or, on conviction on indictment, to imprisonment for a term not exceeding 2 years, or a fine, or both.

2 Except for an immediate Prohibition Notice, an Inspector has power to withdraw a notice or extend the period specified in the notice, before the end of the period specified in it. If you wish this to be considered you should apply to the Inspector who issued the notice, but you must do so before the end of the period given in it. Such an application is not an appeal against this notice.

3 The issue of this notice does not relieve you of any legal liability for failing to comply with any statutory provisions referred to in the notice or to perform any other statutory or common law duty resting on you.

4 Your attention is drawn to the provision for appeal against this notice to an Industrial Tribunal. Details of the method of making an appeal are given below, see also Section 24 of this Act. This appeal should be sent to: The Secretary of the Tribunals, Central Office of the Industrial Tribunals, Southgate Street, Bury St. Edmunds, Suffolk IP33 2AQ (for England and Wales) or The Secretary of the Tribunals, Central Office of the Industrial Tribunals, St Andrew House, 141 West Nile Street, GLASGOW G1 2RU (for Scotland only).

The appeal must be commenced by sending in writing to the Secretary of the Tribunals a notice containing the following particulars :

(a) the name of the appellant and his address for the service of documents;

(b) the date of the notice, or notices, appealed against and the address of premises or place concerned;

(c) the name and address, as shown on this notice, of the respondent;

(d) particulars of the requirements or directions appealed against; and

(e) the grounds of appeal.
A form which may be used for appeal is attached.

Time limit for appeal
A notice of appeal must be sent to the Secretary of the Tribunals within 21 days from the date of service on the appellant of the notice, or notices, appealed against, or within such further period as the tribunal considers reasonable in a case where it is satisfied that it was not reasonably practicable for the notice of appeal to be presented within the period of 21 days. If posted the appeal should be sent by recorded delivery.

The entering of an appeal does not have the effect of suspending this notice. Application can be made for the suspension of this notice to the Secretary of the Tribunals, but the notice continues in force until a Tribunal otherwise directs.

An application for suspension of the notice must be in writing and must set out:

(a) the case number of the appeal, if known, or particulars sufficient to identify it; and

(b) the grounds on which the application is made. (It may accompany the appeal.)

The rules for the hearing of an appeal are given in The Industrial Tribunals (Improvement and Prohibition Notices Appeals) Regulations 1974 (SI 1974 No. 1925) for England and Wales and The Industrial Tribunals (Improvement and Prohibition Notices Appeals) (Scotland) Regulations 1974 (SI 1974 No. 1926) for Scotland.

ENVIRONMENT AND SAFETY INFORMATION ACT 1988

Notes 1 to 7 omitted from this copy

Improvement Notice

There is no mention of improvement or prohibition notices in the Electricity at Work Regulations, since these are already covered by the HSW Act.

Where an inspector considers that a person is contravening any relevant statutory provision (the law), or has contravened it in circumstances that make it likely that the contravention will continue or be repeated, he can issue an Improvement Notice. The inspector must specify what legal requirements he (or she) thinks are being broken and give the reasons for that opinion. The inspector must give at least 21 days to put matters right, since this is the time limit for an appeal against the notice to be made. The Inspector will normally attach a Schedule to the notice specifying ways in which the recipient can comply with the Notice.

The Inspector can extend the period of notice providing an appeal has not been made, or the expiry date specified in the Improvement Notice has not been passed.

Where an appeal to an industrial tribunal is made against an Improvement Notice, the tribunal may either cancel or affirm the notice. If the tribunal affirms the notice it may, if they so wish, leave the Improvement Notice in its original form, or modify it.

Where an appeal is made then the Improvement Notice is suspended until such time as the notice is finally disposed of or the appeal is withdrawn. If the tribunal affirms the notice then, unless modified by the tribunal, the date for the improvement is the same as that stated on the Improvement Notice.

The inspector may, but is not forced to, give information as to what remedial work is required to put matters right. Any such information, including reference to any Approved Code of Practice, may also give a choice between different ways of remedying the contravention.

Prohibition Notice

Where in the opinion of the inspector any work being carried out or about to be carried out involves the risk of serious personal injury he can issue a Prohibition Notice. Where the risk of injury is imminent, the prohibition takes immediate effect and the work activity must stop immediately. If not, the Prohibition Notice will be a deferred one stating the work activity must be stopped within a specified time.

The inspector can issue the notice even if the law at that point in time is not being broken, if the law has been broken then he must say so in the notice, he must also state the matters that will give rise to the risk and direct that the activities which constitute the risk shall not continue. As with an Improvement Notice, although not obliged to, the inspector will usually provide a schedule describing ways in which compliance with the notice can be achieved.

Except for a Prohibition Notice which has immediate effect, the Inspector can withdraw a notice or extend the period specified in the notice; an application to have a notice withdrawn or the period extended should be made to the Inspector issuing the notice.

An appeal against a Prohibition Notice does not suspend the notice. If an appeal is to be made, it has to be made within 21 days of the date the notice was issued; similarly, an application can be made for the notice to be suspended. Both an appeal or a suspension of the notice must be made to the Secretary of Tribunals.

Further details are given in Section 24 of the Health and Safety At Work etc. Act 1974, the rules for the hearing of an appeal are given in: The Industrial Tribunals (Improvement and Prohibition Notices Appeals) SI 1974 N°1925 for England and Wales and SI 1974 N° 1926 for Scotland.

Management of Health and Safety at Work Regulations 1999 (MHSWR)

These regulations require employers to make an assessment of the risks to the health and safety both of employees and non-employees, see Regulation 3. Similar duties are placed on the self-employed.

Regulation 3 (MHSWR): Risk assessment

(1) Every employer shall make a suitable and sufficient assessment of -
> *(a) the risks to the health and safety of his employees to which they are exposed whilst they are at work; and*
> *(b) the risks to the health and safety of persons not in his employment arising out of or in connection with the conduct by him of his undertaking,*

for the purpose of identifying the measures he needs to take to comply with the requirements and prohibitions imposed upon him by or under the relevant statutory provisions and by Part II of the Fire Precautions (workplace) Regulations 1997.

(2) Every self-employed person shall make a suitable and sufficient assessment of-
> *(a) the risks to his own health and safety to which he is exposed whilst he is at work; and*
> *(b) the risks to the health and safety of persons not in his employment arising out of or in connection with the conduct by him of his undertaking,*

for the purpose of identifying the measures he needs to take to comply with the requirements and prohibitions imposed upon him by or under the relevant statutory provisions.

(3) Any assessment such as is referred to in paragraph (1) or (2) shall be reviewed by the employer or self-employed person who made it if -
> *(a) there is reason to suspect that it is no longer valid; or*
> *(b) there has been a significant change in the matters to which it relates;*

and where as a result of any such review changes to an assessment are required, the employer or self-employed person concerned shall make them.

(4) An employer shall not employ a young person unless he has, in relation to risks to the health and safety of young persons, made or reviewed an assessment in accordance with paragrapphs (1) and (5).

(5) In making or reviewing the assessment, an employer who employs or is to

employ a young person shall take particular account of-

(a) the inexperience, lack of awareness of risks and immaturity of young persons;

(b) the fitting-out and layout of the work place and the workstation;

(c) the nature, degree and duration of exposure to physical, biological and chemical agents;

(d) the form, range, and use of work equipment and the way in which it is handled;

(e) the organisation of processes and activities;

(f) the extent of the health and safety training period provided or to be provided to young persons; and

(g) risks from agents, processes and work listed in the Annex to Council Directive 94/33/EC[8] on the protection of young people at work.

(6) Where the employer employs five or more employees, he shall record -

(a) the significant findings of the assessment; and

(b) any group of his employees identified by it as being especially at risk.

As far as the electrical installation and equipment are concerned, this regulation is stipulating that a risk assessment has to be carried out concerning any work activity concerned with electricity. MHSW Regulation 3 (6) then stipulates that where the employer or self-employed person employs five or more persons he has to record the significant findings of the assessment and any employees that the assessment finds are especially at risk.

For example, the assessment could reveal that there was a risk from live equipment when carrying out electrical maintenance and that the electricians were especially at risk. The risk assessment would have to go further than this simple statement and identify the particular risks involved. The next step would be to comply with MHSW Regulation 5

Principles of prevention to be appplied

Where an employer implements any preventative and protective measures he shall do so on the basis of the principles specified in Schedule 1 to these regulations.

*Regulation5 (MHSWR) : **Health and safety arrangements***

(1) Every employer shall make and give effect to such arrangements as are appropriate, having regard to the nature of his activities and the size of his undertaking, for the effective planning, organisation, control, monitoring and review of the preventative and protective measures.

(2) Where the employer employs five or more employees, he shall record the arrangements referred to in paragraph (1).

Having made the assessment of the risk, the method or procedure adopted to minimise or eliminate those risks can now be determined. The amount of planning will depend upon the size of the undertaking, but in a simple case could mean the careful selection of equipment that would reduce or eliminate the risk of say electric shock. 'Organisation' in the regulation means having a management structure which allows originally unforeseen risks to be identified at the lowest level in the company and for these risks to trigger a change in the safety procedures set out by a higher level of management in the company. Control is also a management procedure, but this time the object is to ensure that the specified safety procedures are being implemented. Monitoring and review links the previous items together so that the management procedure is constantly reviewing the safety measures adopted. This would then work in conjunction with MHSW Regulation 3 (6) detailed above.

The HSW Act Section 2(3) already requires an employer of five or more persons to prepare a written statement of their policy on health and safety and the organisation and arrangements for carrying out that policy. Regulation 4 of the MHSW regulations adds important detail to this requirement, in particular the need to ensure that arrangements are effective.

Having a Code of Safe Working Practice could form part of the procedures mentioned above.

Provision and Use of Work Equipment Regulations 1998 (PUWER)

The PUWE Regulations should not be considered in isolation. A risk assessment should be carried out as called for by MHSW Regulation 3 (1) and the information obtained used for the correct selection of equipment using the PUWE Regulations.

Where the equipment is to be purchased it should comply with the Supply of Machinery (Safety) Regulations (SM Regulations) - which will probably satisfy most of the PUWE Regulation requirements. Where existing equipment is to be used it must not only comply with the PUWE Regulations but also Section 6 of the HSW Act.

The scope of the regulations is covered by Regulation 2.

Regulation 2 (PUWER): Interpretation

(1)   In these regulations, unless the context otherwise requires- "the 1974 Act" means the Health and Safety at Work etc. Act 1974;

__employer__ except in regulation 3 (2) and (3) includes a person to whom the requirements imposed by these Regulations apply by virtue of regulation 3 (3)(a) and (b);
__essential requirements__ means requirements described in regulation 10(1);
__the executive__ means the Health and Safety Executive;
__inspection__ in relation to an inspection under paragraph (1) or (2) of regulation 6-
(a) means such visual or more rigorous inspection by a competent person as is appropriate for the purpose descibed in the paragraph
(b) where it is appropriate to carry out testing for the purpose, includes

testing the nature and extent of which are appropriate for the purpose;
*"**power press**" means a press or press brake for the working of metal by means of tools, or for die proving, which is power driven and which embodies a flywheel and clutch;*
*"**thorough examination**" in relation to a thorough examination under paragraph (1),(2),(3) or (4) of regulation 32-*
    (a) means a thorough examination by a competant person;
    (b) includes testing the nature and extent of which are appropriate for the purpose described in the paragraph;
*"**use**" in relation to work equipment means any activity involving work equipment and includes starting, stopping, programming, setting, transporting, repairing, modifying, maintaining, servicing and cleaning;*
    "**work equipment**" means any machinery, appliance, apparatus, tool or installation for use at work (whether exclusively or not);

and related expressions shall be construed accordingly.

(2) Any reference in regulation 32 to 34 or Shedule 3 to a guard or protection device is a reference to a guard or protection device provided for the tools of a power press.
(3) Any reference in regulation 32 to 33 to a guard or protection device being on a power press shall, in the case of a guard or protection device designed to operate while adjacent to a power press, be construed as a reference to its being adjacent to it.
(4) Any reference in these Regulations to -
(a) a numbered regulation or Schedule is a reference to the regulation or Schedule in these Regulations so numbered; and
(b) a numbered paragraph is a reference to the paragraph so numbered in the regulation in which the reference appears.

As can be seen from 2(1) the scope of the definition is very wide and includes cleaning and transporting the equipment. Transporting could range from a simple two wheeled trolley or wheelbarrow to a fork lift truck.

The definition 'work equipment' is also very wide in its scope ranging from a screwdriver to a company owned motor vehicle. It includes such things as: portable drill, soldering iron, drill bit, computer, test instruments or test equipment.

By virtue of PUWE Regulation 3, the regulations apply to employers, the self employed, to any person who has control to any extent of non-domestic premises made available to persons as a place of work where items of work equipment are provided; or to any person to whom the Factories Act 1961 CH 34 applies.

The suitability of work equipment is covered by the following regulation.

Regulation 4 (PUWER): Suitability of work equipment

(1) Every employer shall ensure that work equipment is so constructed or adapted as to be suitable for the purpose for which it is used or provided.

(2) In selecting work equipment, every employer shall have regard to the working conditions and to the risks to the health and safety of persons which exist in the premises or undertaking in which that work equipment is to be used and any additional risk posed by the use of that work equipment.

(3) Every employer shall ensure that work equipment is used only for operations for which , and under conditions for which, it is suitable.

(4) In this regulation "suitable" means suitable in any respect which it is reasonably foreseeable will affect the health or safety of any person.

This regulations means that the employer has to make certain that the equipment has been designed, constructed and manufactured for the work for which it is going to be used. Additionally, consideration has to be given to the place where the work equipment will be used. For example, consideration has to be given to the type of portable electric tools used down a wet well, the voltage allowed for such tools and the electrical protection provided to disconnect the tool in the event of a fault.

Maintenance

(5)   (1) Every employer shall ensure that all work equipment is maintained in an efficient state, in efficient working order and in good repair.

(2) Every empployer shall ensure that where any machinery has a maintenance log, the log is kept up to date.

Inspection

(6)   (1) Every employer shall ensure that, where the safety of work equipment depends on the installation conditions, it is inspected -

   (a) after installation and before being put into service for the first time; or

   (b) after assembly at a new site or in a new location,

to ensure that it has been installed correctly and is safe to operate.

(2) Every employer shall ensure that work equipment exposed to conditions causing deterioration which is liable to result in dangerous situations is inspected -

   (a) at suitable intervals; and

   (b) each time that exceptional circumstances which are liable to jeopardise the safety of the work equipment have occurred,

to ensure that health and safety conditions are maintained and that any deterioration can be detected and remedied in good time.

(3) Every employer shall ensure that the result of an inspection made under this regulation is recorded and kept until the next inspection under this regulation is recorded.

(4) Every employer shall ensure that no work equipment -

   (a) leaves his undertaking; or

    (b) if obtained from the undertaking of another person, is used in his undertaking,

unless it is accompanied by physical evidence that the last inspection required to be carried out under this regulation has been carried out.

    (5)   This regulation does not apply to -

        (a) a power press to which regulations 32 to 35 apply;

        (b) a guard or protection device for the tools of such power press;

        (c) work equipment for lifting loads including persons;

        (d) windingapparatus to which the Mines (Shafts anbd Winding) Regulations 1993 [6] apply;

        (e) work equipment required to be inspected by regulation 29 of the Construction (Health, Safety and Welfare),Regulations 1996 [7].

PUWE Regulation 5 covers maintenance of the work equipment and the keeping of maintenance logs up-to-date. PUWE Regulation 6 addresses the necessary inspections required where the safety of the work equipment depends on the installation conditions, as well as making requirements for the intervals betrween inspections and for records of such inspections to be kept. PUWE Regulation 7 is provided to comply with the EEC directive and as such requires no action by the employer if he is already complying with existing legislation.

Regulation 7 (PUWER): Specific risks

    (1) Where the use of work equipment is likely to involve a specific risk to health or safety, every employer shall ensure that -

    (a) the use of that work equipment is restricted to those persons given the task of using it; and

    (b) repairs, modifications, maintenance or servicing of that work equipment is restricted to those persons who have been specifically designated to perform operations of that description (whether or not also authorised to perform other operations).

    (2) The employer shall ensure that the persons designated for the purposes of sub-paragraph (b) of paragraph (1) have received adequate training related to any operations in respect of which they have been so designated.

Regulation 8 (PUWER): Addresses, information and instructions, as follows:

    (1) Every employer shall ensure that all persons who use work equipment have available to them adequate health and safety information and, where appropriate, written instructions pertaining to the use of the work equipment.

    (2) Every employer shall ensure that any of his employees who supervises or manages the use of work equipment has available to him adequare health and safety information and, where appropriate, written instructions pertaining to the use of the work equipment.

    (3) Without prejudice to the generality of paragraphs (1) or (2), the information

and instructions required by either of those paragraphs shall include information and, where appropriate, written instructions on -

(a) the conditions in which and the methods by which the work equipment may be used;

(b) foreseeable abnormal situations and the action to be taken if such a situation were to occur; and

(c) any conclusions to be drawn from experience in using the work equipment.

(4) Information and instructions required by this regulation shall be readily comprehensible to those concerned.

Penalties

The HSW Act makes provisions under Section 33 for penalties to be imposed. There are many items listed, a contravention of any of which would constitute an offence. However, the offences which concern most people are those covering the failure to comply with Sections 2 to 7 of the Act or failure to comply with an improvement or prohibition notice.

Since all health and safety legislation is produced under the HSW Act a failure to comply with particular health and safety regulations such as, the Electricity at Work Regulations, attracts the penalty provisions of the HSW Act.

All offences can be tried either in the Magistrates Courts (Sheriff Court, without jury, in Scotland) or the Crown Court (Sheriff Court, with jury, in Scotland). All cases start in the Magistrates Court, but depending upon the seriousness of the case the HSE can ask for the case to be tried in the Crown Court. Similarly the defendants can ask for the case to be tried in the Crown Court; the final decision rests with the magistrates.

Where the case is tried in the Magistrates Court the maximum penalty for offences covered by Sections 2 to 6 of the HSW Act is £20,000. For all other offences against regulations made under the HSW Act, such as an offence under the Electricity at Work Regulations, the maximum penalty is £5000. Where the offence is for failing to comply with an improvement or prohibition notice the maximum penalty in a Magistrates Court for an individual is imprisonment of up to 6 months or fine up to £20,000 or both. If having been found guilty of failing to comply with an improvement or prohibition notice, they still fail to comply, they may be liable to a further fine of £100 for each day they fail to comply.

For all other offences under the HSW Act such as, obstructing an inspector, or falsely pretending to be an inspector, the maximum fine is £5000 for cases tried in the Magistrates Court.

Where the prosecution takes place in the Crown Court there is no limit to the fine that can be imposed and in the case of certain offences, e.g., contravening a requirement imposed by a prohibition notice, an individual can also be sent to prison for up to two years.

Chapter 4

System construction

EAW Regulation 4 acts as the 'catch-all' requirement of the Electricity at Work Regulations, but has to be read in conjunction with other regulations which deal with particular aspects of electrical safety. Regulation 4 consists of four parts that can be divided into subjects:

- **System construction**
- **Maintenance**
- **Work activity**
- **Safety equipment**

It is easier to understand the regulations and what is required if these subjects are considered separately, since each subject involves most of all the other regulations. System construction can be divided into physical construction and electrical construction.

System construction

EAW Regulation 4(1) specifies that: *all systems shall at all times be of such construction as to prevent, so far as is reasonably practicable, danger.*

This is particularly applicable to the design of electrical installations. However, many installations already existed before the Electricity at Work Regulations were made law, so the requirements for the design for safety should be taken into consideration when existing installations are checked. Regulation 4 can be considered a foundation stone of the regulations, in that to comply with it, reference has to be made to most of the other regulations. Thus Regulation 4 has to be read in conjunction with EAW Regulations 5, 6, 7, 8, 9, 10, 11, 12, and 15.

Electrical safety requires the proper design, installation, inspection and commissioning of an installation. This means planning where equipment is to be installed so that there is adequate access, working space and lighting available for any subsequent work that may be required to be carried out. It also means taking into consideration the competence of the staff that will be used to operate, use and maintain the electrical equipment.

It should be noted that the regulation refers to all systems, with system being defined, as including electrical equipment that may be used. In order to comply with the regulation it is therefore essential to ensure that all electrical equipment is constructed in such a manner that it does not cause danger.

If you have a system that will not cause danger then no precautions are necessary, but the regulations are still applicable.

What the system includes

There is no reference to voltage, portable tools or substations in the regulations since these are part of the system and the regulation applies to all systems.

Systems include:

systems inside and outside, above ground and below ground;

high voltage switchgear and cables;

transforming or converting equipment;

low voltage switchgear, control panels, distribution boards, instrumentation, cables, motors, generators, etc;

final circuit wiring and accessories;

batteries;

instruments used for either indicating and recording data or for testing;

portable generator sets;

portable tools, equipment, electric typewriters, computers etc;

items that are not connected but can readily be connected to the system.

These are the items that you have to ensure are of such construction as to prevent danger. There is the additional requirement to comply with the Provision and Use of Work Equipment Regulations, where the term 'use' is very widely interpreted to include all activities including stopping, starting, repair, modifying, maintaining, servicing and cleaning.

Construction includes both the physical construction and electrical construction of the system. Physical construction will be dealt with first.

Physical construction

Physical construction means taking into consideration the following items:

* damage,

* corrosion,

* danger of fire and of explosion,

* layout,

* environmental conditions.

Damage

Consideration has to be given to the location of electrical equipment, so that it cannot be damaged. This is done by making certain that it is out of the way of materials being handled during production, by checking that the electrical supplies to machines are installed in such a way that they cannot be damaged and by ensuring the equipment is located so that danger will not arise by say, fork lift trucks running into the equipment. Equipment can be dented or scratched providing no danger will arise from such damage. Damage also extends to portable electrical equipment, the most vulnerable parts of which are the lead and plug used with such equipment.

Corrosion

As far as corrosion is concerned, consideration has to be given to the existing conditions and those that can arise in the future where the electrical equipment is installed or used. Corrosion can occur in various ways, one of the obvious ones is due to water; where equipment is installed in a damp location or outside it should be of the weatherproof type. Where hosing down is taking place then the equipment should be suitable for the pressure and direction of the water jets. Guidance on the type of enclosure to be used can be found in BS EN 60529:1992, (see Chapter 10).

Water is not the only cause of corrosion, chemicals can attack various types of materials. A check should be made to ensure that any solvents used in the manufacturing process or for cleaning, or materials that may be installed at a later date will not affect the installation materials. For instance, certain types of granular insulation leach out the polymers in PVC cable making it soft and tacky, with the effect that the conductors move through the insulation towards each other causing a fault to occur, which can cause a fire.

Care has also to be taken when aluminium conductors are connected to brass or other metals with a high copper content. The remedy here is to use Densal Paste on the terminations.

Another instance of corrosion is where metal conduit is installed in contact with building materials containing magnesium chloride, corrosive salts, lime or where it is in contact with acidic woods, such as oak.

Danger of fire and of explosion

Fire can be caused by the overloading of circuits that are not equipped with the correct type and rating of protective device. Cables can overheat due to the overload, setting fire to adjacent flammable materials such as wood. A break in the conductor can cause sparking with the ultimate breakdown and ignition of the insulation. Fire can also be caused by flammable materials being in close proximity to electrical equipment that works at a high temperature. Tungsten lamps generate a large amount of heat resulting in the light fitting being raised to a high temperature; this is particularly so with tungsten halogen light fittings.

Additionally, fire can be caused by loose joints in equipment or cable terminations. Where, owing to a loose joint, sparking takes place under oil it produces a flammable vapour which can ultimately result in explosion. Consideration must also be given to taking the necessary precautions to stop the spread of burning oil and fumes that could arise should an explosion in the equipment occur owing to a fault.

Regulation 10 of the EAW Regulations specifies that:

> *Where necessary to prevent danger, every joint and connection in a system shall be mechanically and electrically suitable for use.*

There is no reference in the regulation to 'so far as is reasonably practicable' so it must be complied with.

The correct type of equipment has to be selected for the conditions applicable in the area where it is located for example; equipment selected must be correct for the types of explosive gases, liquids, vapours or dusts in that area. Powders being blown along pipes or liquids being poured into, or extracted from, storage tanks cause static electricity to build up; an earthed object approaching such a pipe or tank can cause a flash-over. Precautions must therefore be taken to eliminate static electricity building up and discharging in an explosive atmosphere. Flameproof motors can overheat when they become coated with flammable materials that can interfere with the normal cooling of the motor, causing the coating on the motor to burst into flame.

Fire and explosion can also be caused by short-circuit currents or earth fault current and protective devices should be selected to contain the destructive energy produced by such currents.

Environmental conditions

Environmental conditions are the subjects of EAW **Regulation 6:**

Electrical equipment which may reasonably foreseeably be exposed to -

> *(a)   mechanical damage;*
> *(b)   the effects of the weather, natural hazards, temperature or pressure;*
> *(c)   the effects of wet, dirty, dusty or corrosive conditions; or*
> *(d)   any flammable or explosive substance, including dusts, vapours or gases, shall be of such construction or as necessary protected as to prevent, so far as is reasonably practicable, danger arising from such exposure.*

This regulation covers adverse or hazardous environments, some of which have already been discussed. The most important aspect of EAW Regulation 6 is that the equipment selected has to take into consideration conditions which are reasonably foreseeable. For example, if equipment designed for use in domestic premises is taken into a factory or used on a construction site, it is reasonably foreseeable that it can become damaged, or that it can be affected by the weather and that a danger could arise.

EAW Regulation 6 is specifying that equipment has to be either so constructed or protected to prevent danger arising from any of the conditions given in the regulation.

Conditions within the factory environment can be quite adverse depending upon the type of work being undertaken, consideration has therefore to be given to the type of cable and electrical equipment installed and how it is protected and how cables are terminated.

Electrical system construction

Electrical construction has to take into account:

- the risk of electric shock,
- the risk of electric burns,
- overcurrent,
- type of protective device,
- access to equipment,
- selection of equipment,
- commissioning and testing the system,
- maintenance of the system,
- competence of the personnel operating and maintaining the system.

All these items have to be taken into account when the system is designed or checked. In addition consideration has to be given to the layout of the system and the correct selection of equipment. However, since most work places will have been constructed before the Electricity at Work Regulations and the legislation for the EEC Directives came into force, and since they now apply to premises that the previous regulations did not cover, the design parameters of existing installations should be checked to ensure that the system is initially safe.

The electrical construction of the system requires a great deal of consideration, so the different subjects have been divided into separate chapters since the regulations involved interact on each subject.

Object of the EAW Regulations

The object of the regulations is to ensure the need for 'live' working is critically examined and, wherever possible, reduced if not eliminated.

Chapter 5

System Construction - Protection against electric shock

One of the greatest risks with electricity is the risk of electric shock. This is not confined to those who are repairing or maintaining the electrical equipment, although those who operate and maintain electrical equipment are at greater risk of receiving an electric shock.

An appreciation of the principles of reducing the risk of electric shock is important. It is impossible to remove the chance of a person receiving an electric shock at some time or other, but an understanding of the principles will enable an assessment to be made of the possible risks and eliminate or minimise them, when considering the construction of the system.

Electric shock current

Most people associate an electric shock with voltage, but it is current that kills, although at high voltage burns become a contributory factor to death.

The level of current passing through the body has various affects which are summarised in Figure 5.1

Current (mA)	Effects on the body (hand to hand)
1.5	First noticable sensation
2.5	Tingling on palms
5	Cramp starts
7.5	Hands stiffening 'let go' still possible
10-15	Cramp increases; limit of 'let go'
25-30	Severe cramp extending to the thoracic region
30-50	Increase in blood presure; heart irregular
50-60	Respiratory system affected; loss of consciousness
60-75	Lower threshold of heart fibrillation

Fig 5.1 - Effects of current passing through the body

For those who are not familiar with the units of electricity a milliamp (mA) is 0.001 amperes (amps), 100 mA is therefore only 0.1 amps. For comparison a one kilowatt fire or kettle takes approximately 4 A or 4000 mA, which gives some idea of how little current is needed through the body to kill.

For a given current path through the body, the danger to persons depends mainly on the magnitude and duration of the current flow. The current through the body is only limited by two items; the external resistance of the surface in contact with the body and the body's own resistance.

As far as the resistance of the external surface is concerned, this is dependent upon the type of material it comprises and the environmental conditions, for example the amount of moisture present. The environmental conditions can have an enormous influence on the amount of current flowing through the body, for instance a dry wooden floor would increase the resistance to current flow by about 4000 ohms; a steel floor nothing. In general, the requirements for protection against electric shock assume normal environmental conditions. The term 'Normal environment conditions' is taken to mean 'A fully clothed person with shoes and stockings on in a heated room which is carpeted, there may be a little perspiration on the hands'. For all other conditions the protection requirements have to be more severe.

The impedance to current flow through the human body consists of an internal impedance and skin impedance. The value of the internal impedance usually depends on the current path and to some degree on the surface area of contact, this impedance can, however, be considered to be mostly resistive. When the surface area of contact is only a few sq. mm. there is an increase in internal body resistance. The impedance of the skin is dependent upon: the voltage, frequency, length of time the current flows, surface area, pressure of contact, temperature, and the amount of moisture on the skin. When the current is increased the skin impedance falls, similarly increasing the frequency also decreases the skin impedance.

Tests have been carried out by the International Electrotechnical Commission (IEC) to try to determine the total body impedance at various touch voltages, the results of such tests being given in Figure 5.2.

Figure 5.2 gives the total body impedance hand to hand or hand to foot with dry conditions, but with a contact area between 50 sq. cm. (3" x 2.6") and 100 sq. cm. (3" x 5.16"). The milliamps can be calculated by dividing the Touch Voltage by the impedance. This is shown for 50% of the population; so that the current effect can be compared with Figure 5.1. For touch voltage greater than 50 volts the total impedance depends less and less on the resistance of the skin and once there is a breakdown of the skin the total impedance approximates to that of the internal body impedance.

The impedance to other parts of the body is not the same as hand to hand or hand to foot, the variations in the impedance to other parts of the body being shown in Figure 5.3.

Touch Voltage	Values for the total body impedance (Ω) that are not exceeded for a percentage (percentile rank) of the population			
	5%	50%		95%
(V)	Ω	Ω	mA	Ω
25	1750	3250	7.6	6100
50	1450	2625	19	4375
75	1250	2200	34	3500
100	1200	1875	53	3200
125	1125	1625	77	2875
220	1000	1350	162	2125
700	750	1100	636	1550
1000	700	1050	952	1500

Figure 5.2 - Total body impedance

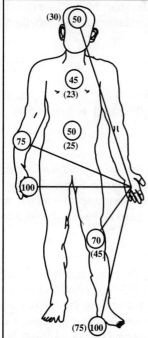

The numbers indicate the percentage of the human body for the path concerned, in relation to the path hand to hand.

The numbers in the circles refer to the current paths from one hand to the part of the body in question.

The numbers in brackets refer to current paths between two hands and the corresponding part of the body.

The impedance from one hand to both feet is 75% of the impedance hand to hand.

The impedance from both hands to both feet is 50% of the impedance hand to hand.

As a first approximation the percentages are also valid for the total body impedance.

Figure 5.3 - Internal impedance of the body as a function of the current path

As can be seen from Figure 5.3 the impedance of both hands to both feet is only 50% of the impedance of one hand to one foot. Since both hands and feet are usually used when using a portable tool, e.g. an electric drill or an electric iron, the shock current is increased.

There are two ways a person can receive an electric shock; either by directly touching a live conductor or live part, or by touching metalwork which has been made live by a fault in the electrical installation. The first is known as direct contact and the second as indirect contact. To comply with the Electricity at Work Regulations protection has to be provided for both types of contact as called for by EAW **Regulation 7**.

All conductors in a system which may give rise to danger shall either -

  (a) be suitably covered with insulating material and as necessary protected so as to prevent, so far as is reasonably practicable, danger; or

  (b) have such precautions taken in respect of them (including, where appropriate, their being suitably placed) as will prevent, so far as is reasonably practicable, danger.

Note that the regulation is referring to 'conductor', which includes any material that will conduct electricity in its solid, liquid or gaseous state. Similarly, *'as necessary protected'* means protecting the live conductors from damage. An example of being suitably placed is the overhead line installed from power stations for the distribution of electricity.

Protection against direct contact

The four basic measures for protection against direct contact are insulation, barriers and enclosures, obstacles and placing out of reach as illustrated in Figure 5.4.

Insulation

Protection is given by the basic insulation of cables and parts required in every installation. The insulation should only be removable by destruction and it should withstand any electrical, mechanical, thermal and chemical stresses to which it may be subjected whilst it is in service. Basic insulation requires mechanical protection.

Barriers or enclosures

Where protection by barriers or enclosures is used to protect against direct contact then the degree of protection must be at least IP2X (or IPXXB) which is the Index of Protection for the standard finger 80 mm long and 12 mm in diameter (the IP Codes are given in Chapter 10 for convenience of readers). Where the opening in equipment has to be larger than IP2X to enable maintenance to be carried out, precautions must be taken to ensure that there can be no unintentional touching of live parts and that persons are warned of the proximity of live parts within the enclosure. Where a top surface of equipment is readily accessible the degree of protection is more stringent and must be at least IP4X.

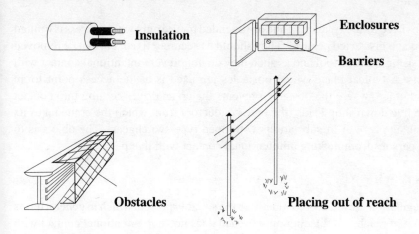

Insulation

Enclosures

Barriers

Obstacles

Placing out of reach

Figure 5.4 - Protection against direct contact

During the maintenance of an installation or the carrying out of new works, enclosures may have to be opened and barriers removed, BS 7671 (the IEE Wiring Regulations) gives four alternative methods of safety against direct contact, which are detailed as follows:

1) The opening of the enclosure or the removal of a barrier must only be possible by using a key or tool. This means that access is limited to skilled persons who should know the dangers and take the necessary precautions.

2) Opening an enclosure or removing a barrier can only be carried out after the supply to live parts has been disconnected and the supply can only be restored after the barriers have been replaced or the equipment reclosed. Isolators interlocked with doors are an example of this type of protection.

3) An intermediate barrier having a degree of protection of IP2X is provided to prevent contact with live parts, the barriers only being removable by using a tool.

Since access is only allowed by using a tool, knurled nuts on covers cannot be used. Care has therefore to be taken when selecting distribution boards to ensure compliance with the requirements for protection against direct contact. Access to the interior of distribution boards is not limited to skilled or instructed persons, quite often barriers are not replaced after work has been completed and many boards have knurled screws for fixing the door, allowing anyone access to the interior.

Obstacles

Obstacles need little explanation and are intended for use only where access is limited to skilled and instructed persons. They should be securely fixed, but can be removed without using a key or tool and as such they do not prevent intentional contact with live parts. A typical place where obstacles are used is at the access point to an overhead crane, where the obstacle prevents the crane driver coming into contact with the live down shop leads (the bare conductors from which the crane takes its electrical supply), or in substations with open type switchgear. The object is to prevent persons from making unintentional contact with live parts.

Arm's reach

EAW Regulation 7(b) allows conductors to be suitably placed, which in general terms means out of reach, but placing out of reach does not stop intentional contact with live parts, so the limit of arm's reach must be increased in areas where long or bulky metallic objects are handled.

Where a barrier or obstacle limits a person's movement, such as a handrail, the limit of arm's reach in the horizontal plane starts at the obstacle unless the degree of protection is greater than IP2X. The limit in the vertical plane is 2.5 m unless there is an intermediate barrier affording a degree of protection greater than IP2X (i.e. IP3X or larger number).

Protection against indirect contact

When the primary insulation fails, a fault occurs which can give rise to danger, because even though the live electrical parts and conductors cannot be touched, the metalwork round the electrical conductors or equipment can become live. There are five ways to try and limit the degree of danger.

1) Earthed equipotential bonding and automatic disconnection of the supply.
2) Using Class II equipment or equivalent insulation (double insulated).
3) Non-conducting location.
4) Earth-free local equipotential bonding.
5) Electrical separation.

Each of the above items will now be looked at in turn, but in reverse order.

Electrical separation and earth free locations

Items 3, 4 and 5 are usually associated with the testing and repair of electronic equipment.

Radio and television repair bays can be very dangerous owing to the chassis of such equipment being connected to one pole of the supply. The first requirement is to make the area earth free; the first consideration being for the supply to be made through an isolation transformer manufactured to BS 3535. Such a transformer can either be double insulated or have an earthed metallic screen between the primary and secondary windings as well as a high insulation value between windings. This arrangement limits the risk of a connection between the primary and secondary windings developing if a fault occurs in the transformer.

To ensure an earth free area the output from the transformer is not earthed; the floors and walls should also be of insulating material. Precautions should also be taken to ensure that there are no metal windows or central heating pipe work in the area and heating should be out of arm's reach.

A high level of illumination is required, which should be designed to eliminate shadows, making local bench lighting unnecessary; the lighting fittings being out of arm's reach.

Even with these precautions, danger is still present in the small test room from the possibility of the chassis of two items of equipment being connected to different poles of the supply, as illustrated in Figure 5.5. To reduce this risk, the earth terminal of socket outlets should not be connected to earth but bonded together at the test bench.

If there is more than one test bench, additional precautions are necessary to stop the possibility of voltage appearing between test benches, with arrangements being made for each test bench to be supplied from its own independent winding on the isolation transformer.

The testing and repair of industrial electronic equipment can be more dangerous, since such equipment is likely to be contained in metal cases which must be earthed, giving rise to the danger of touching live parts and the earthed metal casing. In these situations the supply should be through an isolation transformer and a circuit that limits the current through the human body to a safe value by tripping the circuit breaker which disconnects the supply from the circuit.

The above procedures reduce the risk of electric shock, but do not reduce the risk of flash over caused by a tool getting across both poles of the supply. The secondary circuit should therefore be protected by a device that will limit the energy let through when a short-circuit occurs, to comply with EAW Regulation 11. The same device should also give overload protection and be suitable for any prospective short-circuit current to comply with EAW Regulation 5. Both these regulations will be explained more fully later.

Non-conducting location

The comments already made for electrical separation and earth free locations are also applicable to non-conducting locations. The non-conducting location is primarily intended to prevent simultaneous contact with parts that may have a different voltage on them due to the failure of the insulation of live parts. As such, its use is confined to special locations which are under supervision.

Where there is a possibility that exposed conductive parts can have a different voltage on them owing to insulation failure, then a person must not be able to make simultaneous contact between two exposed conductive parts or between an exposed conductive part and an extraneous conductive part.

Protective conductors are not allowed nor is an earthing contact allowed in any socket outlet or luminaire supporting coupler.

Tests have to be carried out at three points on each surface, including the floor, to ensure a minimum insulation resistance is obtained between each surface and the main protective conductor for the installation. Additionally one of the points of test has to be within 1 and 1.2 metres of any extraneous conductive parts in the location.

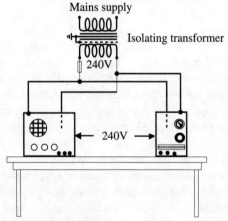

Figure 5.5 - Danger repairing two equipments on the same bench

Class II equipment - Double insulation

Class II equipment is equipment in which protection against electric shock does not rely on basic insulation alone, but incorporates additional safety precautions such as double insulation or reinforced insulation, there being no provision for earthing the appliance. In accordance with BS 2754, Class II equipment is marked by the symbol shown in Figure 5.6.

Figure 5.6- Class II symbol

BS 2754 is not a specification, it only gives recommendations for the requirements and tests to be included in specifications, for the construction of electrical equipment for protection against electric shock.

Double insulated tools have in addition to the basic insulation of the components another layer of insulation to give added protection, this can take the form of an insulated case round the tool such as, a portable drill. It relies on the tool being withdrawn from service if the casing becomes damaged to the extent that the integrity of the double insulation is no longer available. Such tools also suffer from the disadvantage that the leads to such equipment, although having two layers of insulation, are easily damaged. For safety the supplies to portable tools should be taken from a supply protected by a residual current device (RCD). (The operation of an RCD is explained on page 64.)

The above is in contrast to Class I equipment which requires all metallic parts being connected to a protective conductor in the fixed installation so that they are connected to the installation's main earth bar.

As far as the fixed installation is concerned a protective conductor has to be installed to all double insulated items used in an installation, such as switches and ceiling roses, to allow for the insulated accessory being changed to a metal one at a later date.

Reduced voltage systems

Another method of reducing the risk of electric shock is the use of 110 volt tools supplied from a transformer manufactured to BS 3535. The voltage to earth for a single phase transformer is 55 volts with the centre point earthed, and 65 volts to earth with a three phase transformer with the neutral point earthed. Such an arrangement is shown in Figure 5.7. It should be noted that the reduced voltages given above are not SELV (extra-low voltage).

Consideration should be given to using 110 V centre tapped transformers with portable tools in all locations where the floor does not have an insulating covering or where a large area of the body is in contact with earth. The factory is one such area, where concrete floors add little or no resistance to the flow of current through the body. The importance of using a reduced voltage system can be seen clearly in the following calculation.

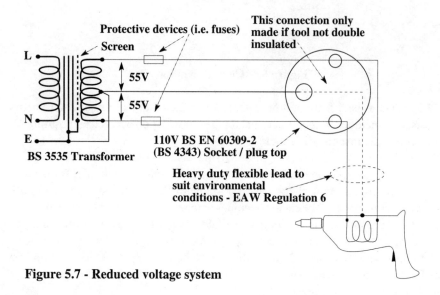

Figure 5.7 - Reduced voltage system

Using the minimum resistance values from Figure 5.2 will give an approximate comparison of the amount of current flowing through the body with 50 volts to earth and 220 volts to earth.

$$I_{50V} = \frac{50\,V}{1450\,\Omega} = 34\,mA \qquad I_{220V} = \frac{220\,V}{1000\,\Omega} = 220\,mA$$

As can be seen from the figures, a person receiving an electric shock at 50 volts stands a much better chance of surviving than when the voltage is at 220 volts. At 220 volts the individual is in serious trouble (even if the maximum body resistance is used in the calculation the current is 103 mA which is sufficient to kill). In both cases the speed of disconnecting the circuit is important.

Isolation transformers

Using a transformer to isolate equipment from the mains supply only goes part of the way to providing protection against electric shock, as can be seen from Figure 5.8.

When the installation is new, a person touching one of the circuit conductors connected to the transformer will not receive an electric shock. However, after the first fault has occurred an electric shock will be received as the current has now a return path through the faulty earth connection.

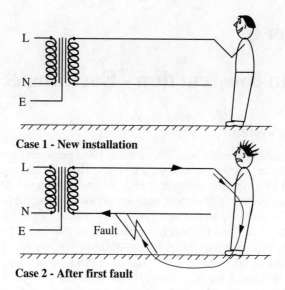

Case 1 - New installation

Case 2 - After first fault

Figure 5.8 - Electric shock with isolated supply

Connections

Part of the protection against electric shock is to ensure that all joints and connections are properly made. This means that all connections, including those made to portable equipment, plug tops and through couplers, as well as the connections at switchgear and distribution boards, are mechanically and electrically sound. In addition it also means checking that the clamp holding the cable into the equipment, plug top and through couplers is securely holding the cable. This is important since many accidents occur due to the cable being pulled out of the plug top, with the result that the earthing conductor becomes detached from its connection and touches the phase conductor connection making the case of the equipment live. The earthing conductor having become disconnected means that a person touching the metal casing of the equipment (indirect contact) will receive a severe electric shock.

Earthed equipotential bonding and automatic disconnection

The majority of installations rely on item 1 (earthed equipotential bonding and automatic disconnection of the supply) for protection against indirect contact. This subject requires a considerable amount of explanation so it will be dealt with in the next two chapters.

Chapter 6

System construction - Earthing & Bonding

Earthing systems

Earthing and bonding are fundamental methods of protecting against indirect contact and as such are worthy of their own chapter. The way an installation is earthed is designated by a type of system of which the installation is a part.

There are five types of system, each one of which describes how the installation's exposed-conductive-parts (metalwork) are earthed. The five systems are TN-S, TN-C, TN-C-S, TT and IT. This last system is not allowed to be used in the U.K. for distributing electricity to the public. Additionally, the installation is part of the system; without the installation all you have is a type of supply.

Before looking at the diagrams it is as well to consider for what each designated letter in the system stands. The T specifies that the source of energy is earthed at one or more points, it is also used to indicate a direct connection with earth. The N specifies that the installation's exposed-conductive-parts are directly connected back to the source earth, which is usually the neutral point of the source. The S indicates that the protective conductor connecting the exposed-conductive-parts back to the source earth is a separate conductor throughout the system (i.e. in the supply and in the installation) whereas the C indicates that it is combined with the neutral throughout the system (i.e. the neutral acts as the protective conductor as well). The letter I indicates that the source is either not connected with earth or is earthed through a high impedance.

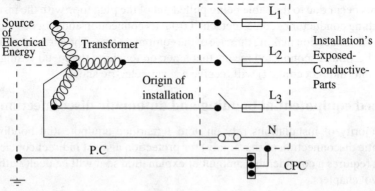

Figure 6.1 - TN-S system

Figure 6.1 illustrates the TN-S system where PC stands for protective conductor and CPC for circuit protective conductor. Note that the protective conductor is separate back to the main earth.

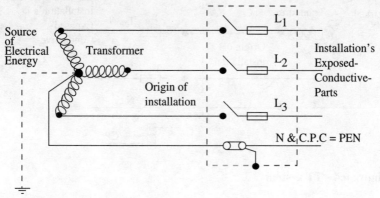

Figure 6.2 - TN-C system

Figure 6.2 shows the TN-C system where the neutral conductor is also used as the protective conductor (PC). This makes it a protective earthed neutral (PEN conductor).

Figure 6.3 shows the TN-C-S system where the protective conductor is combined with the neutral in part of the system (usually in the supply) and separate in the rest of the system (usually the installation).

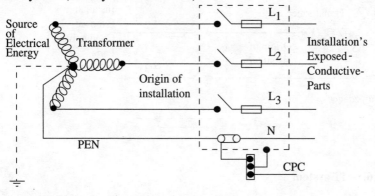

Figure 6.3 - TN-C-S system

Figure 6.4 illustrates the TT system which is usually applicable in rural areas where the electricity supplier cannot provide an earth. Here the installation's exposed-conductive-parts are directly connected with earth.

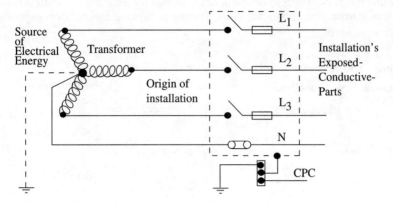

Figure 6.4 - TT system

The IT system is shown in Figure 6.5, however, this is the system that is not allowed to be distributed to the public in the U.K. by the electricity suppliers. Cables in an IT system are usually double insulated and a protective conductor is not distributed. It relies on the impedance at the source limiting the magnitude of the fault current, however, the system does have disadvantages.

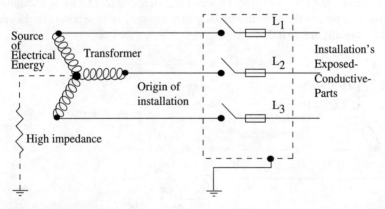

Figure 6.5 - IT system

The U.K. uses, in general, the principle of earthing equipment as a safeguard to protecting persons touching exposed-conductive-parts made live by a fault (indirect contact). Other methods of protection, such as double insulation, have been introduced as far as actual appliances are concerned.

Regulation 4.1 of the EAW Regulations in specifying that the system construction shall prevent danger includes the earthing of exposed conductive parts and Regulation 8 details the requirements.

Regulation 8 : (EAWR) *Precautions shall be taken, either by earthing or by other suitable means, to prevent danger arising when any conductor (other than a circuit conductor) which may reasonably foreseeably become charged as a result of either the use of a system, or a fault in a system, becomes so charged; and for the purposes of ensuring compliance with this regulation, a conductor shall be regarded as earthed when it is connected to the general mass of earth by conductors of sufficient strength and current-carrying capability to discharge electrical energy to earth.*

This regulation makes the specific point concerning conductors becoming charged and is obviously concerned with any material that will conduct electricity in its solid, liquid or gaseous state. Where a fault occurs between a phase conductor and an exposed conductive part a voltage will appear on the exposed conductive part, i.e., it will become charged. This charge must be removed as quickly as possible to prevent danger.

There is a further requirement that any conductor used for earthing must have sufficient strength and current-carrying capability. When a fault occurs a large current flows in the phase and protective conductor. Regulation 8 requires the protective conductor to be suitable for carrying such a large current and to be capable of withstanding the electrical and mechanical stresses created by the large fault current.

It is not the intention with this book to become too technical, so a simplified explanation will suffice.

The stresses caused by the fault current are heating and magnetic. The heating stress being proportional to I^2t and the magnetic stress to I^2 where I is the fault current and t is the time taken for the protective device to disconnect the circuit.

I^2t is the energy let-through the protective device and this must never exceed the withstand capacity of the protective conductor k^2S^2 where k is a factor dependent upon the conductor's material and insulation and S is the cross-sectional area of the conductor.

For those readers who want to know how to calculate the cross-sectional area required for protective conductors, or to check that existing conductors are suitable, they are referred to the *Handbook on the IEE Wiring Regulations by the author*.

Dangerous earth

Most people think that an earth terminal in an installation is at earth potential with no voltage on it; unfortunately this is just not true. Even with a TN-S system where the protective conductor is separate, a fault in a neighbouring property can produce a voltage at the main earth terminal in the installation. For example, Figure 6.6 shows the protective conductor in a TN-S system. The protective conductor will have a resistance, which in the drawing is shown as R1 up to property one, R2 from property

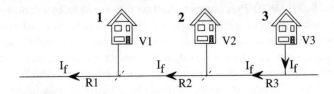

Figure 6.6 - Voltage on earth conductor

one to two and R3 from property two to three. If a fault to earth occurs in property number three a fault current I_f will flow down the protective conductor back to the source earth. This fault current will produce a voltage V1 on the earth bar in property one equal to $I_f \times R1$, a voltage V2 on the earth bar of property two equal to $I_f \times (R1 + R2)$ and a voltage on property three equal to $I_f \times (R1 + R2 + R3)$. In practice these voltages can be high enough to present a hazard to the occupants of the property.

Since the voltage appears on the main earth bar in the property it will also appear on all the exposed-conductive-parts in the building, but the extraneous-conductive-parts, i.e. the metalwork of non-electrical services, may be connected with true earth, i.e. the ground round the building. The voltages V1, V2, or V3 will therefore appear between the exposed-and extraneous-conductive-parts in the building. These voltages can be of such a magnitude as to cause danger, especially if the environmental conditions are not normal.

Where the system is TN-C-S the neutral conductor is used up to the installation as the protective conductor. This means that a voltage will appear on the main earthing terminal and on all exposed-conductive-parts in the installation whenever electricity is used in the installation, since the current returns via the neutral.

A similar situation occurs with the TN-C system where the neutral is used in the installation as a protective conductor. It would therefore be very dangerous if a break occurred in the neutral conductor when it is being used as a protective conductor (PEN conductor).

Referenced conductors

EAW Regulation 9 is concerned with circuit conductors that are connected to earth or a reference point and as such is not referring to protective conductors, but to PEN conductors (protective earthed neutrals).

Regulation 9: *(EAWR) If a circuit conductor is connected to earth or to any other reference point, nothing which might reasonably be expected to give rise to danger* *by breaking the electrical continuity or introducing high impedance shall be placed in that conductor unless suitable precautions are taken to prevent that danger.* Neutral conductors are covered by Regulation 9 since they are connected to a reference point, the reference point being the neutral connection at the source transformer as shown in Figure 6.7.

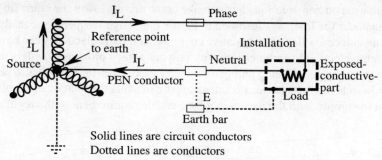

Figure 6.7 - Regulation 9 referenced conductors

The Regulation is trying to prevent referenced circuit conductors, which should be at or about the same potential as the reference point, reaching significantly different potentials, thereby giving rise to possible danger. This means that nothing should be fitted in a neutral that is likely to cause such a potential difference. Thus fuses, thyristors or transistors should not be inserted into neutral conductors or PEN conductors. If a fuse was inserted in a neutral and it blew when a fault occurred, it would leave the equipment live, which would be potentially dangerous. Fuses in the electrical equipment itself are allowed providing the equipment is fed through a plug and socket which can be disconnected before the equipment is opened. Such electrical equipment will, however, need a code of safe working practice. The regulation does not prohibit the use of links or joints in neutral or PEN conductors.

The integrity of the protective conductor, which by definition is not a circuit conductor, relies on EAW Regulation 8 for ensuring that there are no switches, thyristors etc., inserted in it, since the exposed-conductive- parts of the equipment will become charged if the protective conductor (earth) becomes disconnected. It would have perhaps been better if EAW Regulation 9 had started by saying 'that if a conductor or circuit conductor which was connected with earth or to any other reference point', then there would be no doubts that switches, thyristors etc., must not be inserted in protective conductors.

Items becoming charged

EAW Regulation 8 requires precautions to be taken when any conductor, other than a circuit conductor, may reasonably foreseeably become charged. The most common danger of indirect contact has already been discussed, but conductors can become charged in other ways. Induced voltage is one such way that conductors can become charged, the molten metal in an induction furnace can become charged from the electrical coils round the furnace.

High voltage overhead lines can induce a voltage into steel catenary wires where they are used on construction sites to make crane drivers lower the crane jib before passing under the line, as illustrated in Figure 6.8. High frequencies can also give rise to an induced voltage by capacitive coupling, and static electricity can be created by rotating electrical machinery, or with powder pumps blowing powders through pipe work, or by petrol being pumped through a pipe. Consideration has to be given as to how induced voltages may occur as a result of using the system, or a fault in the system to comply with the reasonably foreseeable requirement of the regulation.

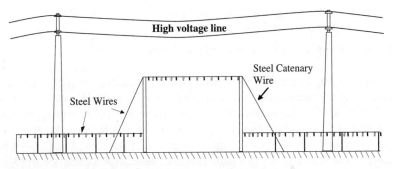

Figure 6.8 - Induced voltages from overhead line

Earthed equipotential bonding and automatic disconnection

To minimise the hazard of a voltage appearing on an exposed-conductive-part, earthed equipotential bonding is used.

This method of protection requires the characteristics of the protective devices, the earthing arrangements for the installation and the impedances of the circuits to be coordinated, so that during an earth fault the voltage appearing between simultaneously exposed-and extraneous-conductive-parts occurring anywhere in the installation will be of such magnitude and duration as not to cause danger.

This requirement coordinates two subjects, equipotential bonding and automatic disconnection, and they are more easily understood if considered separately.

Equipotential bonding

To minimise the magnitude of voltage that can appear between exposed-and extraneous-conductive-parts requires that main equipotential bonding conductors be installed between the extraneous- conductive-parts and the main earthing terminal of the installation. The extraneous-conductive-parts to be bonded include main water pipes, central heating pipes, gas installation pipes, metallic ventilation ducting, exposed metallic parts of the building structure, lightning protection conductors and the metal sheathing of telecommunication cables as illustrated by 1 to 8 in Figure 6.9.

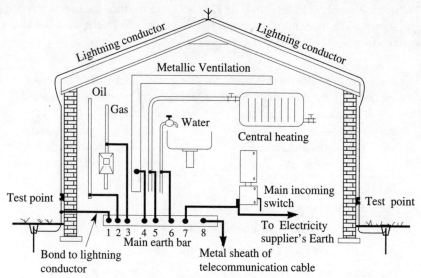

Figure 6.9 - Bonding to internal services (From the *Handbook on the IEE Wiring Regulations* by T. E. Marks)

The bond to the gas installation pipe should be made on the consumer's side of the meter before any branches off the pipe and it is recommended that the bond should be within 600 mm of the meter.

The connection to the mains water pipe should be made as close as possible to its entry into the building. If the supply is through a nonmetallic pipe then the connection should be made to the metallic pipe work on the consumer's side of the stop tap. Where water meters are installed, the connection should be on the consumer's side of the meter, the connection being similar to that for the gas meter.

Where the building is equipped with a lightning protection scheme the lighting conductor has to be bonded to the main installation earth bar. However, the installer of the lightning protection should be informed of the resistance to earth of other installations within the building, including the electrical installation, since the resistance to earth should be the lowest value of any of the individual services when connected to a common earthing system. (BS 6651:1999.)

Size of main equipotential bonding conductors

For TN-S or TT installations the cross-sectional area (CSA) of the main equipotential bonding conductor should be half the cross-sectional area (CSA) of the earthing conductor subject to a minimum size of 6 mm^2 if it is copper. It need not exceed 25 mm^2 if it is copper or the copper equivalent in other metals.

Where the supply is PME (TN-C or TN-C-S systems) then the Electricity Supply Regulations 1988 (amended) specify the bonding conductor size as given in Figure 6.10.

At the time of revision of this book, the Electricity Supply Regulations are soon the be replaced by the Electricity Safety, Quality and Continuity Regulations.

Copper equivalent cross-sectional area of supply neutral conductor	Minimum copper equivalent cross-sectional area of bonding conductor
35 sq mm or less	10 sq mm
over 35 sq mm but not more than 50 sq mm	16 sq mm
over 50 sq mm but not more than 95 sq mm	25 sq mm
over 95 sq mm but not more than 150 sq mm	35 sq mm
over 150 sq mm	50 sq mm

Figure 6.10 - PME bonding conductor sizes

Supplementary bonding

Where there is an insulated break in the extraneous-conductive-parts connected to the main equipotential bonding conductors, then a supplementary bond is required across the insulated joint. The size of this supplementary bond should be the same size as the main equipotential bonding conductor.

A permanent and reliable extraneous-conductive-part, which is connected to a main equipotential bonding conductor, can be used to bond an isolated extraneous-conductive-part that goes out of the building into the ground; again the bonding conductor should have the same cross-sectional area as the main equipotential bonding conductor.

Supplementary bonding is required in special situations such as bathrooms or shower rooms. The object is to create a local equipotential zone so that a voltage appearing on one exposed conductive or extraneous-conductive-part in the area will appear on all the other exposed-or extraneous-conductive-parts, thus stopping a potential difference appearing between the parts.

Bathrooms or shower rooms have to have supplementary bonding, even if the pipe work is connected to the main equipotential bonding conductors. This bonding must include all expose- and extraneous-conductive-parts in the room, even the equipment supplied for a jaccuzzi under baths etc.

Where plastic baths, plastic waste pipes, plastic shower trays and no exposed-conductive-parts are present, it will only be necessary to bond all the extraneous-conductive-parts at one point within the bathroom or shower room. This point will, however, have to be accessible for inspection.

In this situation the cross-sectional area of the supplementary bond can be 2.5 mm² if sheathed or otherwise mechanically protected, otherwise the minimum size required is 4 mm². Where supplementary bonding conductors are installed in the roof void over the bathroom or in the floor, they can be considered as being protected against mechanical damage.

Exposed-conductive-part to exposed-conductive-part

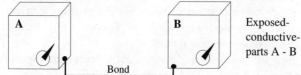

Same conductance as the smallest cpc feeding A or B, providing that it is mechanically protected: otherwise minimum size is 4 mm².

Exposed-conductive-part C to extraneous-conductive-part

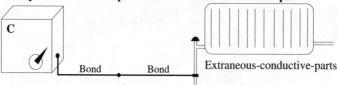

Half conductance of the cpc in 'C' if sheathed or mechanically protected: otherwise minimum size required is 4 mm².

Extraneous-conductive-part to extraneous-conductive-part

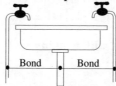

Minimum size 2.5 mm² if sheathed or otherwise mechanically protected: 4 mm² if not mechanically protected.

Figure 6.11 - Minimum size of supplementary bonding conductors (Taken from the *Handbook on the IEE Wiring Regulations* by T. E. Marks)

Where an electrical circuit cannot be disconnected within a time specified in BS 7671, details of which will be given later, either a supplementary bond between exposed-conductive-parts or between exposed-and extraneous-conductive-parts has to be installed or the circuit has to be protected by an RCD. The cross-sectional area of the supplementary bond is determined by its resistance:

$$R \leq \frac{50}{I_a}$$

where R is the total resistance of the bonding conductor and I_a is the current required to disconnect the circuit in five seconds. The bond is, however, subject to minimum sizes as shown in figure 6.11.

Bonding does not remove danger

The object of bonding is to create an equipotential zone so that a voltage appearing on the main earth bar will also appear on all exposed-and extraneous-conductive-parts within the zone. It can be seen from Figure 6.9 that a voltage appearing on the main earth bar will appear on all other metalwork owing to the electrical connections (bonding conductors) connected to the earth bar. This does not mean, however, that a person will not receive an electric shock.

Figure 6.12 shows a simple case of an extraneous-conductive-part (radiator and pipe work) being bonded to the main earth bar. When a fault occurs inside the exposed-conductive-part, the voltage appearing on the exposed-conductive-part (metal case of the electrical equipment) will be $I_f (R_2 + R_3)$ with respect to the

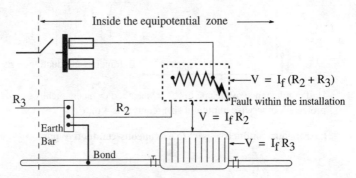

Figure 6.12 - Shock voltage with bonding

earthed point at the source of supply (the electricity distributors transformer). It can also be seen from Figure 6.12, that even when the extraneous-conductive-parts are bonded to the main earth bar, a voltage will appear between an exposed-conductive-part and an extraneous-conductive-part when a fault occurs in the installation. The bond has only reduced the magnitude of the voltage.

The Electricity at Work Regulations require that, as far as is reasonably practicable, the construction of the system should not cause danger. This means taking into account the adverse conditions given in EAW Regulation 6. For instance, the kitchen of the works or office canteen will probably have a quarry tiled floor, stainless steel work benches, metal sinks, as well as electrical machinery. Staff will generally be working with plenty of water about, with benches being washed down, pans being filled with water and of course washing of utensils. It would therefore be reasonable to bond all the metal work (i.e. the exposed and extraneous conductive parts) together within the kitchen, creating a local equipotential zone. This would then remove the risk of electric shock from indirect contact as far as is reasonably practicable.

Another requirement of EAW Regulation 6 would be to ensure that the electrical accessories, for example socket outlets and plug tops, are the correct type for the environmental conditions. As far as the kitchen is concerned this would mean checking if weatherproof accessories have been installed where they are likely to get splashed with water. A further precaution would be to use socket outlets with switches which interlock with the plug top, so that the plug can only be removed after the socket is switched off.

Areas not covered by the equipotential zone

Equipotential bonding only covers the area inside the building. A greater danger exists with equipment used outside the building but deriving its supply from within the building. The danger arises from the fact that people outside are in direct contact with earth, i.e., there are no floor coverings to help insulate them from earth.

One of the requirements of EAW Regulation 6 is to foresee any environmental conditions that are likely to arise, so consideration has to be given to equipment that is used within the building that may be taken for use outside.

Another problem with electrical equipment used outside the building, but obtaining its supply from within the building, is the conductor earthing the equipment (known as the Circuit Protective Conductor, C.P.C. for short). This C.P.C. will be connected to the earthing system within the building, so a voltage on the earthing system inside the building will also appear on the exposed-conductive-parts of the electrical equipment used outside.

If the equipment is portable, protection can be given by using a residual current device (explained later). Where the electrical equipment is permanently wired up (known as fixed equipment) outside the building, and is within arm's reach of other metallic items (extraneous-conductive-parts), then one solution is to bond the exposed-conductive-parts to the extraneous-conductive-parts and connect them to earth with a local earth rod, as shown in Figure 6.13.

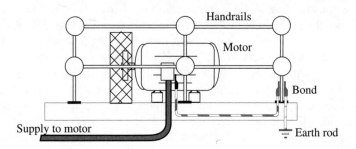

Figure 6.13 - Bonding and earthing outside-extraneous-conductive parts

The four foot long 10 mm diameter copper clad steel earth electrode is ideal for this situation. It is not required to carry current, but to hold down the exposed-and extraneous-conductive-parts to earth potential; or at the very least create a local equipotential zone.

Connections

Part of the protection against electric shock is to ensure that all joints and connections are properly made, which is particularly applicable to earthing and bonding. All joints and connections have to be properly constructed to comply with EAW Regulation 10, this is an absolute Regulation so it is mandatory.

Regulation 10: (EAWR) Where *necessary to prevent danger, every joint and connection in a system shall be mechanically and electrically suitable for use.*

Making certain connections and joints are properly made to comply with Regulation 10 also means taking into consideration the environmental conditions that are applicable. This means that EAW Regulation 10 has also to be read in conjunction with EAW Regulation 6 which is concerned with environmental conditions.

Chapter 7

System Construction - Automatic disconnection

It has already been shown that inside the equipotential zone a voltage will appear between an exposed-conductive-part and an extraneous-conductive-part if a phase to earth fault occurs. But EAW Regulation 4(1) specifies:

Regulation 4(1): (EAWR) All *systems shall at all times be of such construction as to prevent, so far as is reasonably practicable, danger.*

The voltage appearing on exposed-conductive-parts due to a fault is dangerous and to comply with EAW Regulation 4(1) this voltage must be removed as quickly as possible. It cannot be removed instantaneously since protective devices need a finite time to operate. The actual disconnection time required is dependant upon the environmental conditions and whether a person is likely to be in contact with exposed-conductive-parts at the instant of the fault; thus the disconnection time allowed for socket circuits is less than that for fixed equipment.

Inside the equipotential zone, the maximum disconnection time allowed by BS 7671 is dependent upon the voltage to earth U_0. For a voltage to earth in the range 230 V to 277 V the disconnection time allowed is 0.4 seconds for circuits supplying portable equipment intended for manual movement during use, hand-held Class I equipment and socket-outlets circuits. For fixed equipment the disconnection time allowed is 5 seconds.

The disconnection time of 0.4 seconds can be increased to 5 seconds, providing the impedance (resistance) of the protective conductor all the way back to the main earth bar is limited to a maximum impedance of 50 V divided by the current required to disconnect the circuit in 5 secs. This arrangement is not allowed for equipment outside the equipotential zone. Outside the equipotential zone portable and hand-held equipment must also be protected by a residual current device (RCD).

The disconnection times given above are for normal environmental conditions i.e. warm room, carpeted floor, person fully clothed. Where the environmental conditions are not normal then disconnection times have to be reduced or protection has to be given by residual current devices.

The speed at which a protective device will disconnect a circuit is dependant upon the size of the fault current, which in turn is dependant upon the value of the phase earth loop impedance Z_s. It is important to understand what an earth fault is and the path the current takes when such a fault occurs.

Figure 7.1 shows a TN-S system (separate protective conductor back to the source of energy) starting at the source of energy, with the feeder cables up to the origin of the circuit and from the origin to the end of a final circuit. Meters have been omitted for clarity.

The equipment is shown with a phase to earth fault, which for calculation purposes is always assumed to be of negligible impedance, i.e. there is no resistance between the phase conductor and the exposed conductive part.

At the instant of the fault, current will flow through the phase winding of the transformer, along the phase conductor up to the fault, and then along the protective conductor back to the transformer. This is called the phase earth loop, and the magnitude of the current is only limited by the impedance of the transformer phase winding, the phase conductor, and the impedance of the protective conductor.

These are represented in the diagram by Z_A, Z_B, Z_1, Z_2, Z_C, and Z_D.

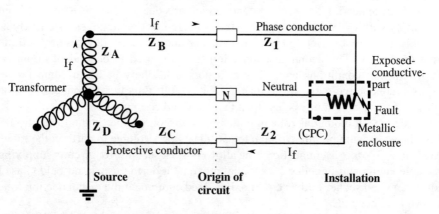

Figure 7.1 - Phase earth loop impedance

The phase earth loop impedance Z_s (sometimes just referred to as the earth loop impedance) is obtained from the addition of all the individual impedances in the loop i.e.

$$Z_s = Z_A + Z_B + Z_1 + Z_2 + Z_C + Z_D$$

In the diagram impedances Z_A, Z_B, Z_C, and Z_D are all external to the installation and are referred to as Z_E. The impedances Z_1 and Z_2 are in the installation and are referred to as Z_{inst}.

The calculation of phase earth loop impedance is carried out using the following formula.

$$Z_s = Z_E + Z_{inst}$$

The earth loop impedance Z_s determines the amount of fault current that will flow with a phase to earth fault and this in turn determines the disconnection time of the protective device.

There is a close relationship between automatic disconnection and sizing the protective conductor, since the phase earth loop impedance Z_s determines the current flowing in the CPC.

Since reactance only needs to be taken into account for the conductor sizes 25mm² or greater, impedance in the above formula can be replaced by resistance for small cables, i.e. Z_{inst} is now the resistance of the phase and circuit protective conductor; R_1 and R_2 respectively.

The values of resistance or impedance used should be based on the temperature the conductors will reach with the fault current flowing, since the fault current will raise the conductor temperature increasing its resistance. This increase in resistance would then lower the fault current to a point where the disconnection time of the protective device could be increased, as shown in Figure 7.2. The temperature used for determining the conductor resistance is the average of the conductor's operating temperature and the limit temperature of the conductor's insulation; for normal PVC this is 115 °C.

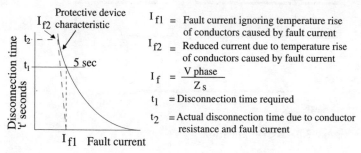

I_{f1} = Fault current ignoring temperature rise of conductors caused by fault current

I_{f2} = Reduced current due to temperature rise of conductors caused by fault current

$I_f = \dfrac{V \text{ phase}}{Z_s}$

t_1 = Disconnection time required

t_2 = Actual disconnection time due to conductor resistance and fault current

Figure 7.2 - Effect of conductor temperature rise on fault current

As the resistance of conductors used in calculations to determine Z_s is based on a temperature far in excess of ambient temperature, the value of Z_s will also have to be worked out for the temperature at which the installation will be tested, since the conductors will be at a lower temperature than if they were carrying fault current.

The conductors must also be designed to withstand the fault current I_f to comply with EAW Regulation 5.

Regulation 5: (EAWR) No *electrical equipment shall be put into use where its strength and capability may be exceeded in such a way as may give rise to danger.* The protective conductor is also covered by EAW Regulation 8 given in the last chapter, since it specifies that earthing conductors must be of sufficient strength and current carrying capacity. Additionally, the circuit must be protected by a protective device to comply with EAW Regulation 11; this, however, is the subject of a later chapter.

Methods of disconnection

There are two methods available for disconnecting a circuit for protection against indirect contact (metalwork made live by a fault). The first is overcurrent protection, which means using either a fuse or circuit breaker, the second is the use of a residual current device.

The operation of a residual current device (abbreviated to RCD or RCCB residual current circuit breaker) is best explained by looking at Figure 7.3.

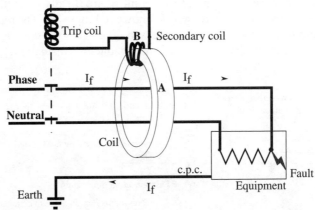

Figure 7.3 - RCD operation

Residual Current Device (RCD or RCCB)

Consider the circuit without the fault in the equipment. The current flows through the phase conductor into the load setting up a flux in coil 'A' and then flows back through the neutral conductor setting up an equal but opposite flux in coil 'A' cancelling out the flux generated by the phase conductor. When an earth fault occurs not all the current passes back down the neutral, so the flux generated in coil 'A' by the phase conductor is not completely cancelled out; this remaining flux links with the secondary coil 'B' generating a voltage which drives a current through the trip coil. When the current passing through the trip coil reaches the residual operating current of the breaker, the unit trips cutting off the supply to the equipment.

It must be noted that the RCD does not give any protection against overloads or short-circuit currents, since in these circumstances the same current would flow down both the phase and neutral conductors. Additionally, the RCD does not limit the size of the earth fault current at the instant of the fault. This is only limited by the phase earth loop impedance Z_s.

The RCD does not prevent a person from receiving an electric shock, what it does do, is limit the time the shock current flows through the body. The RCD can be obtained in a range of operating currents. The most usual one for protecting persons is 30 mA. This means that as soon as the current to earth reaches 30 mA the device will operate, although its operation is not instantaneous.

The severity of the electric shock the person receives will depend upon the environmental conditions, most of which are outlined in EAW Regulation 6, and this should be taken into account when considering the electrical construction of the installation. In practice the RCD will trip with less current than its stated rating, since the British Standard 4293 permits it must trip between 50% and 100% of its rating.

When selecting an RCD make certain the device caters for the d.c. component of the fault current and that it does break both the phase and neutral conductors when it trips.

Disconnection times outside the equipotential zone

It has already been mentioned that the danger of the effects of an electric shock are increased outside the equipotential zone or where the environmental conditions are not normal.

The disconnection times allowed by BS 7671 (the IEE Wiring Regulations) are therefore reduced in these circumstances. The maximum disconnection time allowed outside the equipotential zone for normal TN and TT installations and for bath and shower rooms is 0.4 seconds for permanently fixed equipment. Where persons are using portable equipment outside fed from a socket outlet up to a rating of 32 A, the circuit has to be protected by a 30 mA RCD.

Socket outlets feeding fixed equipment outside the equipotential zone do not need to be protected by an RCD providing the socket outlet cannot be used for hand-held equipment.

Consideration should be given to using RCD protection on socket outlets with a current capacity larger than 32 A, but regard will have to be given to leakage current from the equipment the circuit supplies. Indeed, providing there is no problem with leakage currents, fixed equipment can also have the additional protection of an RCD.

Although RCD protection is not called for within the equipotential zone, this could be considered in the areas having poor environmental conditions, such as those areas which are damp, like kitchens or the factory's canteen. RCD protection is required on stages for electrical equipment used by entertainers.

Chapter 8

System Construction - Protection against overcurrent

An overcurrent can be either an overload current, a short-circuit current, or a phase to earth fault and it is usually simpler to consider these items separately.

When selecting the size and type of electrical equipment, which includes the cables, account has to be taken of the present load on the equipment and any foreseeable future loads that may be connected. Additionally, the electrical equipment must be able to withstand any overload or fault currents that are likely to occur.

An overload is caused by a circuit carrying more current than it was designed for, as in the case of a 3 kW load being connected to a circuit designed only for 1 kW, or due to a motor being mechanically overloaded.

An overload occurs in a circuit which is a healthy circuit, whereas a short-circuit is a fault condition which occurs between live conductors, (which includes the neutral) in conductor connections or in the equipment.

Precautions have to be taken against overcurrents to comply with Regulation 5.

Regulation 5: (EAWR) *No electrical equipment shall be put into use where its strength and capability may be exceeded in such a way as may give rise to danger.*
The stresses referred to as strength and capability means checking that the equipment will withstand the following items:

a) Load currents,
b) Transient overloads,
c) Fault currents,
d) Pulses of current,
e) Currents at various power factors and frequencies,
f) Applied voltage,
g) Transient over-voltages,
h) Environmental conditions.

Similarly, precautions must be taken to ensure that any excess currents are disconnected as soon as possible; this being a requirement of EAW Regulation 11.

Regulation 11: (EAWR) *Efficient means, suitably located, shall be provided for protecting from excess of current every part of a system as may be necessary to prevent danger.*

The protective device installed must break any overcurrent flowing in the circuit before such a current causes a temperature rise detrimental to the conductor, its insulation, joints, terminations, or any material surrounding or in contact with the conductor.

Overload protection

For overload protection, the temperature rise is controlled by ensuring that the protective device installed has a nominal rating equal to, or greater than, the designed full load current of the circuit it is protecting and that the current rating of the circuit conductors are equal to, or greater than, the nominal rating of the protective device.

Additionally, to ensure the temperature rise of conductors or connections is limited, the protective device must have a fusing factor of 1.45 which is obtained as follows:

$$\text{Fusing factor} \quad = \quad \frac{\text{Current causing operation of the device}}{\text{Nominal current rating of the device}}$$

There are several types of protective devices that comply with the fusing factor of 1.45, as listed below:

(a) BS 88 Part 2 or Part 6 fuses, referred to as HRC or HBC fuses
(b) BS 1361 fuses, usually referred to as cartridge fuses
(c) BS 3871, miniature circuit breakers (MCBs)
(d) BS EN 60898, Circuit - Breakers
(e) BS 1362 fuses, a cartridge fuse fitted to a 13 A plug top

Care has to be exercised when using moulded case circuit breakers manufactured to BS EN 60947-2, since the overload elements can usually be changed in such units. The overloads could be changed for higher rating overloads and although still operating with a fusing factor of 1.45 their rating could be more than the current-carrying capacity of the conductors they are supposed to be protecting.

To comply with the requirements of EAW Regulation 5 the electrical construction of the system has to be so designed and installed that electrical equipment is not put into use where danger may arise from the stresses imposed on such equipment. This means the equipment must be capable of carrying any load current or overload current that is likely to occur.

When a circuit conductor is carrying its rated current, it will be operating at a designed temperature suitable for the conductor's insulation, in the case of standard PVC insulation this means that it will be operating at 70 °C. With an overload current flowing in the circuit, which is 45% larger than the full load current, the conductor, along with the terminations and the associated electrical equipment, will increase in temperature, since the protective device usually allows this current to flow for sometimes about four hours (convential time)before it interrupts the circuit. The 1.45 fusing factor therefore limits the temperature rise to an amount which will not cause any deterioration to the conductor's insulation, joints and terminations.

There are devices that allow a larger current than the 1.45 limit to flow under overload conditions before they interrupt the circuit. One such device is the BS 3036 fuse, commonly known as the rewirable fuse, which has a fusing factor of 2. In this case the size of circuit conductor has to be increased so that the working temperature of the conductor before the overload occurs is lower. This is to ensure the temperature rise created by the overload does not exceed the value it would have reached if the fusing factor had been 1.45.

The conductors have therefore to be effectively derated when used with a protective device that has a fusing factor greater than 1.45. The amount they are derated by is a ratio of the two fusing factors, thus 1.45 is divided by the actual fusing factor of the device. In the case of the BS 3036 fuse mentioned above this means:

$$\frac{1.45}{2} \text{ giving } 0.725$$

The current-carrying capacity of the conductor is then multiplied by 0.725 to give a revised current-carrying capacity for the conductor. The simplest way to deal with this is to divide the nominal rating of the protective device (I_n) by 0.725 to give the current-carrying capacity required for the conductor I_z.

Using this relationship for any type of protective device to give the current-carrying capacity of the conductor I_z:

$$I_z = \frac{I_n \times \text{fusing factor of device being used}}{1.45}$$

Positioning of overload devices

Overload protection devices should generally be placed at the point where a reduction occurs in the current-carrying capacity of the conductor. When considering where to install overload protective devices, the circuit must be looked at to determine the factors that will cause a reduction in current-carrying capacity. Where there is a change to the cross-sectional area of the conductor, or a change in the method of installation, overload devices may be required at the point of change. Similarly, if there is a change in the type of cable or conductor, overload protection may be required.

The environmental conditions can affect the current-carrying capacity of a conductor such as, a change in the ambient temperature along the route the conductor takes, or contact with thermal insulation. Grouping with other cables, will also affect the current-carrying capacity of the conductor. These factors will be dealt with more fully later.

Device installed along the run of a conductor

Under certain circumstances overload devices can be installed along the run of a conductor (see Figure 8.1.)

Figure 8.1 - Positioning of overload along the run of a conductor

The overload device can be installed at point 'B' providing there are no branch circuits or outlets for the connection of current using equipment between the points 'A' and 'B'.

A typical example of this arrangement is a motor circuit, where the starter with its overload devices is installed adjacent to the motor.

Omission of overload devices

Under certain circumstances overload protection devices may be omitted (see Figure 8.2.) Overload devices need not be provided at point 'B' if the protective device at point 'A' protects the conductors between 'B' and the load 'C'.

Figure 8.2 - Overload devices can be omitted in certain circumstances

An overload protective device is not required if the characteristics of the load are not likely to cause an overload in the conductors, for example, an overload device is not required in the tails to a consumer unit where the sum of the individual circuit loads will not overload the tails to the consumer unit (in the event of a fault in a circuit, the circuit protective device should operate first). Another example is where the load is a fixed resistive load, as in the case of a heating load, a 3 kW heating load cannot take a larger load than 3 kW.

No overload protective device is required where the unexpected opening of the circuit would give rise to a greater danger than the overload condition. In these situations audible alarms warning that the overload has occurred should be installed.

Finally, overload devices should not be placed in the secondary circuit of current transformers. An open-circuit, or the sudden opening of the circuit, can cause a dangerous peaking high voltage and in all probability would damage the current transformer.

Stress on conductors caused by other factors

The object of sizing cables properly, is to ensure that the temperature of the conductor's insulation does not exceed the temperature it was designed for when carrying its rated current-carrying capacity. The current-carrying capacity of the conductor is based on there being no obstruction to the flow of heat from the conductor, so that an equilibrium is reached and the conductor attains a steady temperature as illustrated in Figure 8.3.

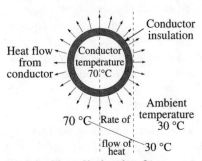

Figure 8.3 - Heat dissipation from a conductor

Factors which can affect the current-carrying capacity of a conductor are given in the following list:

    (a) change in method of installation

    (b) change in cross-sectional area

    (c) change in type of cable or conductor

    (d) change in ambient temperature

    (e) contact with thermal insulation

    (f) grouped with other cables

The way each of the above factors affects the current-carrying capacity of a conductor will now be considered.

Change in method of installation

Where a cable is installed in the open and clipped direct to a building's surface it will be able to dissipate more heat than when it is enclosed in conduit. The method of installation therefore clearly affects the cable's current-carrying capacity.

Change in cross-sectional area

For overload protection the current-carrying capacity of a conductor is based on the temperature that the conductor's insulation will withstand with a continuous current flowing and then being subjected to a 45% overload for about four hours. Reducing the circuit conductor's cross-sectional area for the same current would raise its operating temperature above that permitted for the conductor's insulation.

Change in type of cable or conductor

Since the current-carrying capacity of a conductor is dependent upon the heat being dissipated from the conductor, a multicore cable will carry less current than a single core cable. Changing the material of the conductor will also change its current-carrying capacity because different materials operate with different current-carrying capacities.

Ambient temperature

The current-carrying capacity of the conductor is based on the ambient temperature not exceeding 30 °C, any temperature higher than this will therefore reduce the rate of flow of heat from the conductor and raise the conductor's temperature. In these circumstances the current-carrying capacity of the conductor is reduced, so that its working temperature does not exceed the working temperature of the insulation; in Figure 7.3 this is shown as 70 °C. A derating factor has therefore to be applied to the normal current-carrying capacity of the conductor. As before, this is easier to apply if it is divided into the nominal rating of the protective device (I_n) to give the current-carrying capacity required for the conductor. If the conductor was not derated, its temperature with an overload flowing would take it to a value at which the insulation could be permanently damaged.

Thermal insulation

Thermal insulation reduces the rate of flow of heat from a conductor so the conductor's current-carrying capacity has to be reduced. Tables are provided for those instances where the conductor is in contact with insulation on one side only[1].

Where the conductor is totally enclosed in insulation the reduction is dependent upon the length the conductor is enclosed. The current-carrying capacity has to be multiplied by a factor of: 0.89 for 50 mm, 0.81 for 100 mm, 0.68 for 200 mm, 0.55 for 400 mm and by 0.5 for conductor lengths enclosed in excess of 500 mm.

Grouping of cables

Ambient temperature is not the only occasion that will cause the heat flow from the conductor to be restricted. Bunching or grouping the circuit cables with other circuits will also cause a reduction, since the conductor is now surrounded by other conductors. This will reduce the rate of flow of heat from the conductor and so the normal current-carrying capacity of the conductor has to be reduced, i.e. it has to be derated so that its working temperature does not exceed 70 °C if the cables are PVC.[1]

[1] Detailed explanations of: derating factors, overloads, short-circuit currents, sizing protective conductors, installation design tables, and how to do the calculations, are contained in the Handbook on the IEE Wiring Regulations by T. E. Marks (see Appendix B page 172)

Conductors in parallel

Conductors are allowed to be installed in parallel from the same protective device providing: the conductors are the same type, have the same cross-sectional area, are the same length, follow the same route, and have the same disposition, and providing there are no branch circuits throughout their length. The sum of the current-carrying capacities of all of the cables in parallel can be equal to the nominal rating of the protective device. This can be expressed as in Figure 8.4.

$$\text{Current carrying capacity of each cable} \quad = \quad \frac{\text{Rating of protective device}}{\text{Number of cables in parallel}}$$

The above cannot be applied to ring circuits since they are not parallel circuits.

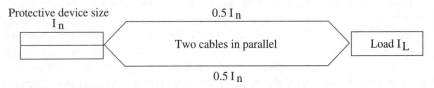

Figure 8.4 - Protection of conductors in parallel

Alternatively, careful assessment of the distribution of currents in the parallel conductors has to be made to ensure that all the conductors are not subjected to overload.

Requirements for providing correct equipment

Electrical machinery, or other current using equipment, will be connected back to a distribution board or switchgear by cables which may even pass through a motor starter.

The first requirement is to ensure that the switchgear is capable of carrying the total load of all the circuits connected to it. Where the equipment connected to the switchgear is not going to work all at the same time, diversity can be taken into account, but this diversity would require re-checking if the equipment was changed at a future date.

Based on the total connected load, the switchgear can be sized to cater for this load and any future load it can be foreseen is likely to be connected at a later date. Leaving spare ways in a distribution board is tantamount to saying the load will be increased in the future. The sizing of cables to the switchgear and from the switchgear to the current-using equipment must take into account any future load and how the cables are installed as outlined above.

A knowledge of the duties the electrical equipment has to perform is essential, and this should then be checked against the manufacturer's specification to make certain that where continuously rated equipment is required the equipment selected is not just suitable for intermittent duty. Similarly, care is needed in the selection of equipment for motors which are frequently started and stopped. This is because of the heating effect on conductors and equipment. When a direct-on-line motor is started, its starting current is some five to seven times its full load current. This increase in current raises the conductor temperature, but this soon disappears if the starting period is not prolonged. Where frequent starting of the motor takes place the conductors do not have the opportunity to cool down, with the result that their working temperature is increased, which could be higher than the working temperature designated for the conductor's insulation. In these cases conductors having a larger current-carrying capacity will need to be installed, and the equipment will require to be continuously rated for the increased heating effect.

Production welding lines can also cause problems due to the current spikes caused by the welders. Although the welders may be operating at different times, the spikes created by each welder can often exceed the rating of the cables and switchgear, and the resultant average of the spikes then gives a constant overload of the cables and switchgear, which causes overheating, resulting in the failure of the cable or switchgear.

EAW Regulation 5 refers to the strength and capability of equipment, so electrical equipment must be sized to take into account transient overloads and pulses of current, as well as overloads. The maximum load that the Electricity Distributor can supply has also to be known to ensure it is not exceeded.

So far, all comments have referred to fixed equipment, but the regulations do not draw any distinction between fixed and portable equipment, it is therefore necessary to make sure that any portable equipment is correctly rated and that all flexible cables to such equipment are correctly sized for the duties they have to perform.

Short-circuit currents

By far and away the biggest stress placed on equipment and conductors is by short-circuit currents, the magnitude of which is only restricted by the impedance of the conductors installed in the circuit.

It must be remembered that electrical equipment includes anything used or intended to be used, so all electrical accessories and cables as well as switchgear, isolators, starters and control panels must be suitable for the conditions to which they may foreseeably be subjected.

The requirement here is to ensure that the switchgear and cables are capable of withstanding the prospective short-circuit current that is likely to flow and requires consideration of the conditions that may be applicable when the fault occurs. This means knowing what the prospective short-circuit current is at the origin of the installation, which is either at the Electricity Distributor's fuses with a low voltage supply, or at the high voltage switchgear where the supply is given at high voltage. It also requires knowledge of the size and type of protective device installed by the Electricity Distributor, since this will affect the energy let through when a short-circuit occurs.

As far as the switchgear, starters etc., are concerned it is the maximum short-circuit current that has to be considered. On a three phase system the maximum fault current will occur with a short of negligible impedance (resistance) at the outgoing terminals of the switchgear. The only limitation to the magnitude of the short-circuit current is the impedance of one phase conductor and one phase of the supply transformer. If the impedance of the phase conductor and transformer phase winding is referred to as Z_p and the phase voltage as V_p then the maximum short-circuit current will be:

$$I_p = \frac{V_p}{Z_p}$$

To ensure the maximum current is obtained the resistance in the calculations of the transformer winding and the cables up to the switchgear should be taken at the lowest temperature that is possible, i.e. with no load on the transformer and allowing for the temperature the cables and transformer could be at when the fault occurs. For instance, if the fault occurs when the power to the factory is switched on after the Christmas holidays when the outside temperature is freezing.

Checking whether the cables will withstand the short-circuit current is done differently, since it is the minimum short-circuit current that is required to ensure the cables will withstand the fault current.

This can be more clearly seen from Figure 8.5. The withstand capacity of the cable can be plotted as a fault current line onto the characteristic of the circuit's protective device, in this case a fuse characteristic. Figure 8.5 shows the fault current line crossing the fuse characteristic.

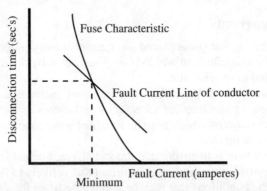

Figure 8.5 - Maximum withstand capacity of a conductor

The minimum fault current and the maximum disconnection time for the conductor is determined by the point the fault current line crosses the fuse characteristic. The point of intersection therefore gives the minimum fault current that must flow in the circuit for the conductor to be protected. The fact that a smaller fault current will damage the conductor can be seen, by drawing a vertical line to the left of the crossover point. The vertical line crosses the fault current line before it reaches the fuse characteristic. The current would therefore be allowed to flow too long and the conductor would be damaged.

This means that calculations should take the resistance of conductors at the temperature they will reach with the fault current flowing to be certain that the fault current never falls below the minimum required. The temperature the conductors will reach with the fault current flowing is achieved in practice by taking the average of the conductor's working temperature and the limit temperature for the conductor's insulation. For example, with normal PVC the working temperature is 70 °C and the limit temperature is 160 °C giving an average of 115 °C. The resistance of the conductor is then worked out at this average temperature. No correction has to be made for reactance in the circuit since this is unaffected by temperature.

In the case of circuit breakers the characteristic means that the minimum and maximum fault currents are required as can be seen from Figure 8.6

This means ensuring the fault current lies between a minimum and a maximum.

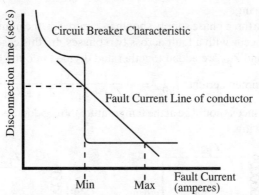

Figure 8.6 - Withstand capacity of a conductor with a circuit breaker

As explained earlier EAW Regulation 11 is concerned with ensuring the system is protected against excess currents. Not all circuits are protected against overload and even those that are still have to be protected against short-circuit currents.

The circuit to an electric heater is one where the protective device only gives short-circuit protection. The circuit to a motor, on the other hand, uses both types of protection; the overloads in the starter give overload protection to the circuit conductors and the motor windings, whereas the protective device in the distribution board only gives short-circuit protection.

Checking that the conductors are protected against short-circuit current involves knowing what the prospective short-circuit current is going to be at the end of the circuit. This in turn requires knowing what the phase impedance is external to the installation, and where the distribution is three phase and neutral. It requires knowing what the neutral impedance external to the installation is as well.

To comply with EAW Regulation 5, which is concerned with withstand capacity, the minimum short-circuit current is required when checking that conductors are protected against short-circuit current. In the case of a three phase and neutral supply, this means taking the impedance of the phase conductor external to the installation, represented by Z_{p1} in Figure 8.7, and adding it to the impedance of the phase conductor Z_{p2} in the installation up to the point of fault, and adding these to the total neutral impedance Z_n, from the point of fault in the installation back to the source. These are then divided into the phase voltage to give the minimum short-circuit current I_{pn} at the point of fault.

$$\text{Minimum short-circuit current} \quad I_{pn} \quad = \quad \frac{V_{ph}}{Z_{p1} + Z_{p2} + Z_n}$$

The impedances taken should be at the temperature the conductors will reach with the fault current flowing.

In the case of a three phase supply shown in Figure 8.8, the minimum short-circuit current I_{pp} will occur with a fault across two phases. In this case, the impedances Z_{p1}, Z_{p2}, Z_{p3}, and Z_{p4} are added together and divided into the line voltage.

$$\text{Minimum short-circuit current} \quad I_{pp} \quad = \quad \frac{V_L}{Z_{p1} + Z_{p2} + Z_{p3} + Z_{p4}}$$

Again the impedances should be at the temperature the conductors will reach with the fault current flowing.

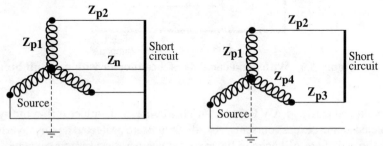

Figure 8.7 - Three phase and neutral short circuit

Figure 8.8 - Two phase short circuit

In both the three phase and neutral and the three phase case, the short-circuit current is then used to determine the time taken for the protective device to disconnect the circuit. This time is then compared with the time the conductors will withstand this current flowing through them determined from the formula

$$t \text{ seconds} = \frac{k^2 S^2}{I^2} \qquad \text{-------- 1}$$

Where k is the thermal capacity factor for the cable, S is the cross-sectional area of the conductor in sq. mm. and I is the short-circuit current. Rearranging this formula gives:

$$I^2 t = k^2 S^2 \qquad \text{-------- 2}$$

Where $I^2 t$ is the thermal energy let through the protective device and $k^2 S^2$ is the thermal capacity of the conductor, it follows that the thermal capacity of the conductor should never be less than the thermal energy let through the protective device.

When the actual disconnection time of the protective device is less than 0.1 seconds, the manufacturer's characteristics are used to determine the $I^2 t$ energy let through the protective device, and this is then compared with $k^2 S^2$, the withstand capacity of the conductor as shown in formula 2.

The protective device has to be suitable for two types of short-circuit current; one that occurs at the outgoing terminals of the device and the other at the end of the circuit fed by the device. Having determined the short-circuit current, the breaking capacity of the protective device, as given by the manufacturer, should be checked, to make certain it is not less than the calculated short circuit current.

Faults to earth

Protecting the system from excess currents also means protecting it against earth fault currents. The formulae given above for short-circuit currents are still applicable, except that in this case the conductors in the circuit are now the phase conductor and the earthing conductor, called protective conductor (CPC). This involves the conductors Z_A, Z_B, Z_1, Z_2, Z_C and Z_D shown in Figure 8.9.

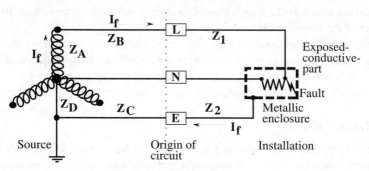

Figure 8.9 - Phase earth-loop-impedance

EAW Regulation 5 requires the electrical equipment to withstand any earth fault currents and EAW Regulation 8 requires that protective conductors are suitable for carrying any fault current that is likely to flow. Protective devices to disconnect such fault currents have to be provided to comply with EAW Regulation 11.

The object here is to ensure that the protective conductor will withstand the electrical and mechanical stresses imposed on it by the earth fault current. Since an earth fault current can be higher than a phase neutral short-circuit current, it is important to check that the breaking capacity of the protective device is not less than the prospective earth fault current at the relevant point in the installation. Similarly, earth fault currents can be less than the short-circuit current between normally live conductors, in which case, a check must be made to ensure that the phase conductor is still protected when an earth fault occurs, because protection of the conductor is determined by the minimum fault current not the maximum. If the protective device is an MCB or MCCB the fault current must lie between a minimum and maximum as illustrated in Figure 8.6.

The thermal withstand of an earthing conductor is checked by using the equation

$$I_f^2 t \leq k^2 S^2$$

where I_f is the fault current, t is the disconnection time for the protective device; k is a factor based on the conductor material, the initial temperature of the conductor at the start of the fault and the limit temperature of the conductor's insulation; S being the cross-sectional area of the conductor in square millimetres.

If the disconnection time of the protective device is less than 0.1 seconds, then $I_f^2 t$ is the energy let through the protective device as given in the manufacturer's characteristics.

The same rules apply to the earthing conductor earthing the neutral point of the supply transformer. The most important role this conductor has is to ensure that the phase angle between the three phase windings is not displaced when an earth fault occurs. In factories or commercial premises all live conductors should be enclosed in earthed metalwork, which should then carry any fault currents back to the neutral point of the transformer.

Flexible connections to electrical equipment must not be overlooked when determining the suitability of the earthing system. They are of paramount importance since a failure at this point will cause the equipment to which it is connected to become charged at mains voltage in direct contravention of EAW Regulation 8.

Voltage drop

The voltage dropped in the conductors must not be overlooked when designing the system, since this can result in insufficient power being developed in the electrical equipment the conductors supply. For instance, if the supply is at 400 volts, the

Electricity Distributors are allowed to deliver their supply at +10%/-6 %. If they take the - 6% and 4% voltage drop is allowed in the conductors of the installation, there will only be 360 volts at a motor terminal box; the additional voltage drop due to the motor starting current will reduce this voltage further. Any further reduction could result in the motor not developing sufficient torque, since the torque of a motor is proportional to the square of the voltage between the stator and the rotor.

Where the electrical supply is provided in accordance with the Electricity Supply Regulations 1988 (as amended) the IEE Wiring Regulations specify that the voltage drop between the incoming supply terminals and the fixed current-using equipment must not exceed 4% of the nominal voltage of the supply.

General installation requirements

Part of the system construction also includes making certain that every joint in the system is mechanically and electrically suitable for use, to comply with EAW Regulation 10.

Regulation 10: (EAWR) *Where necessary to prevent danger, every joint and connection in a system shall be mechanically and electrically suitable for use.*

Electrically suitable means taking into account the current the joint will have to carry, both in normal conditions and when a fault current is flowing. Mechanically suitable means being suitable for the magnetic stress caused by the fault current and the environmental conditions given in EAW Regulation 6, which includes the chemical reaction that can take place at the joint between dissimilar metals.

Regulation 6: (EAWR) *Electrical equipment which may reasonably foreseeably be exposed to-*
  (a) mechanical damage;
  (b) the effects of the weather, natural hazards, temperature or pressure;
  (c) the effects of wet, dirty, dusty or corrosive conditions; or
  (d) any flammable or explosive substance, including dusts, vapours or gases, shall be of such construction or as necessary protected as to prevent, so far as is reasonably practicable, danger arising from such exposure.

In hazardous areas, it would include the correct connection of conduit, or cables to flameproof equipment, that the correct type of seals are made when passing from a hazardous area into a non-hazardous area, that equipment is provided with the correct number of entries and that additional entries are not made in equipment thus negating their certificate.

When designing or laying out the system to comply with EAW Regulation 15, provision has to be made for adequate working space, access and lighting, at all electrical equipment on which, or near which, work has to be carried out.

Regulation 15: (EAWR) *For the purposes of enabling injury to be prevented, adequate working space, adequate means of access, and adequate lighting shall be provided at all electrical equipment on which or near which work is being done in circumstances which may give rise to danger.*

The design of the system has therefore to take into account maintenance that will have to be carried out in the future.

Overloads and short-circuit currents are going to occur in a system at some time. When conductors carry current in excess of their current-carrying capacity, the temperature of the conductor is raised above the designated operating temperature of the conductor's insulation.

This causes a deterioration in the conductor's insulation, which in time will result in a break down of the insulation, tracking will occur between conductors of different polarity resulting in fire.

This is why the current-carrying capacity of conductors is reduced when they are used in an ambient temperature higher than 30 °C, or are grouped, or in contact with thermal insulation. The temperature of the conductor is further increased if an overload occurs, since 45% more current has to flow down the conductor for four hours before the protective device operates.

The design of an installation should take into account the foreseeable increase in current that conductors may have to carry, for instance, if the gas or oil central heating in a building fails, heating is going to be provided by the installation of electric heaters, otherwise staff, students or residents in a hotel are going to be subjected to cold conditions and may ultimately have to be sent home. For instance, if the circuits have not been derated for grouping the cables will overheat and fire could result.

Fault currents also increase the temperature of the conductors, but in this case the effect is immediate, protective devices have therefore to be installed to protect the conductors from both the heating effect and mechanical stresses caused by the large fault currents.

Fault currents do not just flow down the conductors, they also pass through electrical equipment, such as starters, control panels, distribution boards and switchgear. Each item must be capable of withstanding the fault current likely to flow through it and must be selected with care. Specifications and tests carried out on the equipment together with British Standards should be studied and the manufacturer should be consulted where it is not clear how his equipment will perform for the conditions to be applied.

The difference between EAW Regulation 5 and EAW Regulation 11 is that, the former is concerned with ensuring the electrical equipment will withstand these overloads and fault currents without causing danger before such equipment is energised, whereas the latter is concerned with ensuring protective devices are installed to disconnect an overload, a short-circuit current or an earth fault, thereby protecting the system.

Chapter 9

System construction -
Selection and erection of equipment

The selection of equipment is part of the design process, the following items having to be determined before the selection of the electrical equipment can be made.
1. The electrical load at the various points of the building.
2. The size of cables to be used.
3. The prospective short-circuit currents at the various distribution points.
4. Protection against indirect contact is satisfactory
5. That the thermal capacity of protective conductors is satisfactory.
6. Voltage drop is satisfactory for the safe operation of equipment.
7. Environmental conditions.

The switchgear requirements of the installation should be discussed with the manufacturer to ensure that the manufacturer's equipment ratings are suitable for the installation, taking into account the loads, overloads, prospective short-circuit currents and prospective earth fault currents.

Selection of equipment goes further than just making certain it is suitable for short-circuit currents and the connected load. Consideration has to be given to the location of the equipment and this means taking into consideration the environmental conditions outlined in EAW Regulation 6 (given in full on page 79).

Equipment must also be accessible for maintenance and testing to be carried out, to comply with EAW Regulation 15 (page 79) and there must also be adequate lighting.

The area chosen for the equipment should be clean and dry and not used for the storage of flammable or explosive substances. Where equipment is installed in a substation, equipment should be installed to control the spread of fire and extinguish any fire that may occur. Where electrical equipment contains oil or any other forms of flammable dielectric, provision should be made to contain such dielectric should the equipment burst. Provision should also be made for stopping the spread of toxic fumes from burning dielectric spreading to other parts of the building.

The selected electrical equipment should comply with the appropriate British Standard, but where a British Standard takes account of a CENELEC Harmonisation Document, equipment manufactured to a foreign standard can be used if it is based on the same Harmonisation Document. Equipment manufactured to an IEC Standard can also be used, but in this case it is up to the specifier to ensure that it will be no less safe than if manufactured to a British or Harmonised Standard.

Selection of cables

The selection of cables must take into consideration how they are to be installed, making certain that any requirements of EAW Regulation 6 are complied with, for instance, making certain the cables are protected against mechanical damage, that the insulation is suitable for any corrosive substances it may come into contact with, or that the electrical equipment is suitable for use in a hazardous area where there may be explosive dusts, liquids or gasses.

EAW Regulation 7 also requires the conductor to be protected against mechanical damage, additionally it requires the conductor to be insulated,

Regulation 7: *All conductors in a system which may give rise to danger shall either-*
(a) be suitably covered with insulating material and as necessary protected so as to prevent, so far as is reasonably practicable, danger; or
(b) have such precautions taken in respect of them (including, where appropriate, their being suitably placed) as will prevent, so far as is reasonably practicable, danger.

The conductor insulation should ensure that it will give protection against electric shock, that it is suitable for withstanding the stresses imposed on it by the voltage (potential) existing between the conductor and earth, or between the conductor and any other adjacent conductor or electrical component. The selection of cables also includes checking the operating temperature of the equipment they are going to be connected to and making sure the conductor insulation is suitable for that temperature. This can take the form of additional local insulation for example, using glass sleeving on each conductor inside a bulkhead or well glass light fitting.

The current-carrying capacity of conductors should be checked to ensure that the designated operating temperature for the conductor's insulation is not exceeded by the conductors being grouped with other conductors and by being installed in an ambient temperature higher than that allowed by the cable rating. It must also be checked to ascertain that where the conductor is now installed in contact with thermal insulation, or may be liable to be in contact with thermal insulation in the future, its current-carrying capacity has been suitably derated. Where such items are involved the current-carrying capacity of the conductor is obtained from the formula:

$$I_t = \frac{I_n}{G \times A \times T \times S}$$

where I_t = calculated current-carrying capacity required for the conductor
I_n = the nominal rating of the protective device
G = the derating factor for conductors grouped together
A = the derating factor for ambient temperature

T = the derating factor for total enclosure in thermal insulation. See page 71. (Tables are available for contact on one side only.)

S = the factor for devices with a fusing factor greater than 1.45 obtained by the ratio of 1.45 divided by device fusing factor (Page 68).

The individual derating factors 'G', 'A', 'T' and 'S' are only applied to that section of the installation where they are applicable, thus, where a derating factor is not applicable it is replaced by the figure 1 in the above formula.

Where equipment operates at high frequency, any cables used for carrying high frequency current must be sized in accordance with the manufacturer's recommendations since the normal current-carrying capacity tables are not applicable.

Isolation

Consideration has to be given to where isolation is required to enable maintenance to be carried out, since it is now a requirement of the Provision and Use of Work Equipment Regulations (PUWER) as well as the Electricity at work regulations to provide a means of isolating work equipment from every source of energy.

Regulation 19 (PUWER): Isolation from sources of energy

(1) Every employer shall ensure that where appropriate work equipment is provided with suitable means to isolate it from all its sources of energy.

(2) Without prejudice to the generality of paragraph (1), the means mentioned in that paragraph shall not be suitable unless they are clearly identifiable and readily accessible.

(3) Every employer shall take appropriate measures to ensure that reconnection of any energy source to work equipment does not expose any person using the work equipment to any risk to his health or safety.

The type of isolation to be provided involves contemplating the purpose for which the isolation is required, is it only going to be used by electrically trained staff, or are non-electrically trained persons going to use the isolator so that non-electrical maintenance can be carried out?

The distinction is important, since isolators are not designed to make or break load current and non-electrical staff need to be made aware of this fact and trained to switch off the load before operating the isolator. This point is brought out in the Provision and Use of Work Equipment Regulations 1992 (PUWER)

Regulation 8 (PUWER): Information and instructions

(1) Every employer shall ensure that all persons who use work equipment have available to them adequate health and safety information and, where appropriate, written instructions pertaining to the use of the work equipment.

(2) Every employer shall ensure that any of his employees who supervises or manages the use of work equipment has available to him adequate health and

safety information and, where appropriate, written instructions pertaining to the use of the work equipment.

(3) Without prejudice to the generality of paragraphs (1) or (2), the information and instructions required by either of those paragraphs shall include information and, where appropriate, written instructions on-

(a) the conditions in which and the methods by which the work equipment may be used;

(b) foreseeable abnormal situations and the action to be taken if such a situation were to occur; and

(c) any conclusions to be drawn from experience in using the work equipment.

(4) Information and instructions required by this regulation shall be readily comprehensible to those concerned.

Whereas PUWE Regulation 19 is referring to isolation of all forms of power, i.e., steam, hydraulic, electric etc., Regulation 12 of the EAW Regulations specifies that suitable means of cutting off the electrical supply shall be provided where it is necessary to prevent danger. This subject is covered more fully in Chapter 14.

Where a danger could arise due to an error by the person operating the isolator before switching off the load, regard should be given to installing switches instead of isolators, or installing interlocking devices.

The location of the isolator is also important. It must be convenient for its intended use, otherwise there is the probability that staff will try to work on equipment without first isolating it because it is too much trouble to keep walking to the isolator whenever an adjustment has to be made.

Where more than one person is likely to work on equipment a code of practice is required and each person should have their own personal padlock and interlocking tab. This will ensure that the supply cannot be restored by anyone else whilst they are working on the equipment. A typical interlocking tab is shown in Figure 9.1.

Emergency stopping devices

To comply with the Provision and Use of Work Equipment Regulations (PUWER) every piece of work equipment has to be provided with a stop control.

Regulation 15 (PUWER): Stop controls

(1) Every employer shall ensure that, where appropriate, work equipment is provided with one or more readily accessible controls the operation of which will bring the work equipment to a safe condition in a safe manner.

(2) Any control required by paragraph (1) shall bring the work equipment to a complete stop where necessary for reasons of health and safety.

(3) Any control required by paragraph (1) shall, if necessary for reasons of health and safety, switch off all sources of energy after stopping the functioning of the work equipment.

*(4) Any control required by paragraph (1) shall operate in priority to any control
which starts or changes the operating conditions of the work equipment.*

The wording of paragraph one in PUWE Regulation 15 appears quaint, but it must
be remembered that not all work equipment has moving parts for instance, a steam
generator may not have any moving parts, but it can still be very dangerous. Similarly,
the energy source does not necessarily have to be electric.

Figure 9.1 - Interlocking tabs (Courtesy of Seton Ltd.)

Where equipment requires stopping quickly due to a malfunction which may lead to
an accident, or because an accident has occurred, emergency stopping devices are
required. The requirement to provide such controls is now embedded in PUWE
Regulation 16.

Regulation 16 (PUWER): Emergency stop controls

*(1) Every employer shall ensure that, where appropriate, work equipment is
provided with one or more readily accessible emergency stop controls unless
it is not necessary by reason of the nature of the hazards and the time taken for
the work equipment to come to a complete stop as a result of the action of any
control provided by virtue of regulation 15(1).*

*(2) Any control required by paragraph (1) shall operate in priority to any control
required by regulation 15(1).*

Care is required in determining the location of such devices so that they are easily and readily available for anyone to operate.

Where open type conveyors are concerned, emergency stopping devices will be required at points throughout the length of the conveyor, or trip wires can be installed so that the means of stopping the conveyor is available throughout its length. Where trip wires are installed they must be arranged so that a tripping device is fixed at each end of the trip wire and a pull in any direction on the trip wire will cause the trip to operate.

Voltage

All electrical equipment should be suitable for the nominal voltage of the supply and be capable of operating safely at the minimum voltage that can occur owing to voltage drop in the circuit conductors and in the supply to the premises.

All circuits should be checked to establish that the voltage at the electrical equipment is a value within the tolerance recommended by the manufacturer. This includes lighting circuits as well as power circuits. Too much voltage drop in a lighting circuit will reduce the level of illumination given out by the light fitting. It must also be remembered that voltage drop is a product of the conductor's resistance and the current flowing through it, which generates heat in the conductor. This in turn means that there is an I^2R loss in the conductor; power that is lost just heating up the conductor.

The voltage drop in each part of an installation is a compromise and is usually determined by the physical size of the wiring conductors in the final circuit. If the final circuit conductors are too large then they will not fit into the equipment terminals, for example the maximum size of conductor that can be installed into a 13 A ring circuit socket-outlet is two 4 mm^2 cables. The voltage drop in the final circuit is therefore determined by the size of these conductors, which limits the voltage drop in the rest of the distribution scheme. Where the supply to the premises is in accordance with the Electricity Supply Regulations 1988 (amended), then it is considered that the voltage at the equipment will be satisfactory if the voltage drop from the origin of the installation (the incoming supply point) to the end of each final circuit is 4% of the nominal voltage of the supply.

All starting devices for motors above a third of a kW should be equipped with a no-volt release, so that the equipment is stopped should one of the phases feeding the equipment fail. Where no-volt releases are fixed in starting equipment precautions have to be taken to stop such equipment from restarting automatically if danger could arise when the power is restored.

Compatibility

Instances where EAW Regulation 7 can be breached are circuits operating at extra low voltage, or circuits operating at a voltage much lower than the normal mains voltage. These circuits may have insulation only suitable for the lower voltage at which they are operating and such circuits should not be installed with mains voltage circuits unless they have been insulated to the highest voltage present. Even so, it may still be wiser to keep the circuits separate, since the mains voltage circuits can induce a voltage into the lower voltage circuits, affecting the low voltage equipment they operate (telemetering equipment for instance). Emergency lighting circuits and fire alarm circuits should be segregated from all other circuits.

Electrical equipment installed should not cause harmful effects on other equipment or the supply due to; transient over-voltage, rapidly fluctuating loads, starting currents, harmonic currents, mutual inductance or high frequency oscillations etc.

Environmental conditions

The requirements of EAW Regulation 6 mean that the conditions under which the equipment is expected to operate have to be assessed.

Before electrical equipment is specified or purchased, the conditions appertaining to the location where it is to be installed have to be studied; additionally, consideration has to be given to what the conditions may be like in the future. Some of the items to be considered are listed as follows:

Weather - is the equipment going to be exposed to the weather, or is it to be installed in a damp location, is it likely to be affected by the wind, snow or ice? (Overhead lines for instance are affected by snow and ice forming on the conductors and apart from the additional weight and strain placed on conductor supports, it also increases the area the wind force acts upon.)

Dripping water - is the equipment likely to be affected by leaks in roof lights, condensation dripping from roof lights in cold weather, or from leaks in pipework for other services?

Splashing - is the equipment likely to be in an area where hosing down may take place, or is it to be located near washing/ cleaning facilities?

Humidity - is the equipment likely to be subjected to condensation caused by changes in air temperature, or can the condensation form elsewhere and be funnelled onto the equipment?

Atmosphere - is the equipment to be installed in an oily atmosphere where the vapour is likely to condensate onto live parts affecting insulation, or covering air vents to equipment causing the equipment to overheat? Is the atmosphere likely to be explosive from dusts, liquids or gas-air mixtures?

Dusts - is the equipment likely to be affected by dusts caused by production, or used in the production process, such as, the dust created in an iron foundry, sawdust, cotton waste in a cotton mill, coal dust, which may create a flammable situation?

Fungus - is the atmosphere warm and humid so that fungus and mould growth is likely to occur on the insulation of the equipment ?

Fumes - is the equipment to be in an area where there are volatile or gaseous chemicals which are likely to cause damage to bare metal parts, or the insulation on conductors?

Vermin - precautions will have to be taken where vermin have access to equipment. Rats have been known to get into high voltage equipment causing an explosion, they have also been known for chewing the PVC insulation off conductors.

Natural hazards - additional precautions will be required if the electrical equipment is to be installed in an area subject to livestock, or where it can be affected by the roots or branches of trees, tides, or can be affected by solar radiation which leaches out the polymers from some plastic materials.

Temperature - account should be taken of the temperatures in which the electrical equipment is to operate, for instance the current rating of PVC cables is based on an ambient temperature of 30 °C. Electrical equipment is usually designed to operate within a defined temperature range. Equipment designed for use in Britain may be completely unsuitable for use in Far East countries, even the performance of HRC fuses is affected by high temperatures.

Pressure - equipment may also be affected by the pressure under which it is to operate, similarly altitude affects the performance of equipment.

Static electricity - static electricity can be caused by the movement of liquids, solids and gasses laden with suspended liquid or solid matter. The blowing of powders through pipes, or the filling of petrol tanks creates static electricity, as do liquids being stirred in a bowl.

The important consideration is to ensure that precautions are taken to eliminate the build up of static electricity and to arrange for its safe discharge to earth. This is particularly important in a hazardous area, but the area does not have to be a hazardous area for danger to be present. An explosion can occur when powder is blown through pipes in a bakery if the pipework is not earthed; this also means paying attention to the resistance across joints in the pipework. Where rotating machinery is involved, brushgear can be installed to make contact with rotating shafts, discharging any build up of static electricity.

The hazards mentioned above means careful selection of the enclosure for the electrical equipment, which should be selected in accordance with the IP Codes for the conditions in which it is to be used; to stop persons touching live parts the minimum category of IP code adopted should be IP2X or IPXXB.

The requirements of EAW Regulation 6 are equally applicable to portable electrical equipment, as well as the fixed electrical equipment in the installation.

Chapter 10

Index of protection

EAW Regulation 6 requires the correct selection of equipment for the environmental conditions that can foreseeably occur. The IP (Index of Protection) codes can be of assistance in determining the type of enclosure required to comply with EAW Regulation 6. They give a means of specifying your requirements to manufacturers or determining whether manufacturers' equipment is suitable for the conditions envisaged. This chapter explains the IP codes and how the numbering system works.

Full information on the IP codes is given in BS EN60529, which follows IEC 529 by providing the optional extension of the IP codes by an additional letter A, B, C, or D indicating that the actual protection of persons against access to dangerous parts is higher than indicated by the first characteristic numeral. Additionally, a supplementary letter can be used after the second characteristic numeral giving supplementary information.

The basic code only needs to contain two characteristic numbers, the letters IP being followed by two numerals. On the continent a third number is used to indicate the degree of protection against mechanical impact. (UTE C 20-010 French Standards.) It is regrettable that these were not incorporated into the European standard. They have, however, been incorporated into this chapter for completeness.

Figure 10.1 shows how the characters are laid out in the code, except that in the UK the third characteristic numeral is not shown.

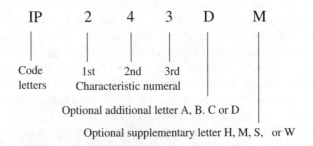

Figure 10.1 - Outline of the code

Details of each characteristic number and letter will be given with a brief explanation of how to use the IP codes. Detailed information is in BS EN 60529.

First characteristic numeral

The first characteristic numeral defines two types of protection. First it defines what degree of protection the enclosure gives against persons gaining access to dangerous parts and secondly what degree of protection the enclosure gives against the ingress of solid foreign bodies. To comply with the protection against access to dangerous parts adequate clearance must be provided between the test probe and the dangerous parts.

0   No protection against contact with dangerous parts.
No protection of equipment against the ingress of solid objects.

1   Protected against access to dangerous parts with the back of the hand.
Protected against solid foreign objects exceeding 50mm in diameter.

2   Protected against dangerous parts inside an enclosure by fingers 12mm in diameter and 80mm long and solid foreign objects 12.5 mm or greater in diameter.

3   Protected against persons touching dangerous parts by a 100 mm × 2.5mm diameter probe and no penetration of solid foreign bodies 2.5 mm diameter.

4   Protected against persons touching dangerous parts. No penetration of solid foreign objects 100mm diameter or greater.

5   Protected against persons touching dangerous parts. Protected against the ingress of dust in such quantities that it would interfere with the safe or satisfactory functioning of the equipment.

6   Protected against persons touching dangerous parts. Protected against the ingress of dust.

Second characteristic numeral

The second characteristic numeral defines the degree of protection against the ingress of water. Compliance with any characteristic numerals up to 6 also means compliance with any lower numeral. However, an enclosure which has the characteristic numeral 7 or 8 is not suitable for categories 5 or 6 (water jets), unless these categories are also specified. This is usually done by specifying both degrees e.g., IPX5/IPX7.

0   No protection against the ingress of water.

1   Protected against vertically falling drops of water which will have no harmful effects on the enclosure.

2   Protected against vertically falling drops of water which will have no harmful effect when the enclosure is tilted at any angle up to 15 ° from either side of the vertical.

3   Protected against water sprayed at an angle up to 60° from the vertical position, which shall have no harmful effects on the enclosure.

4   Protected against water splashed from any direction, which will have no harmful effects on the enclosure.

5   Protected against water projected in jets against the enclosure from any direction shall have no harmful effects.

6   Protected from water projected in powerful jets against the enclosure from any direction, which shall have no harmful effects.

7   Protected against water entering the enclosure in quantities causing harmful effects when the enclosure is temporarily immersed in water under defined conditions of time and pressure.

8   Protected against water entering the enclosure in quantities that could cause harmful effects when the enclosure is immersed for an indefinite period in water. The conditions being more severe than numeral 7. The conditions having been agreed between the manufacturer and user.

Third characteristic numeral

The third characteristic numeral is not part of BS EN 60529, but is derived from the French standard mentioned earlier. It is useful since it specifies the degree of protection against mechanical impact that equipment will withstand.

0   No protection

1   Protected against an impact energy of 0.225 joule, i.e. impact of 150 g from a height of 150 mm.

2   Protected against an impact energy of 0.375 joule, i.e. impact of 250 g from a height of 150 mm.

3   Protected against an impact energy of 0.5 joules, i.e. impact of 250 g from a height of 200 mm.

5   Protected against an impact energy of 2.0 joules, i.e. impact of 500 g from a height of 400 mm.

7   Protected against an impact energy of 6.0 joules, i.e. impact of 1.5 kg from a height of 400 mm

9   Protected against an impact energy of 20.0 joules, i.e. impact of 5 kg from a height of 400 mm.

Optional additional letter

An additional letter A, B, C or D has been introduced which indicates that the protection offered to persons against contact with dangerous parts in the enclosure is higher than that indicated by the first characteristic numeral. The letter can also be used on its own to indicate that it is the only protection against touching dangerous parts. In these circumstances the first characteristic numeral is replaced by an X with the letter following it. It also implies that the protection against the ingress of foreign bodies is not specified.

A   Protected, by there being adequate clearance from dangerous parts, against the back of the hand touching dangerous parts.

B   Protected, by adequate clearance from dangerous parts, against a 12mm diameter × 80 mm long finger touching dangerous parts.

C   Protected, by adequate clearance from dangerous parts, against access with a 2.5 mm in diameter × 100 mm long tool.

D   Protected, by adequate clearance from dangerous parts, against access with a 1.0 mm in diameter × 100 mm long wire.

Supplementary letter

Supplementary letters have been introduced to give more information on the degree of protection. These supplementary letters can be introduced into product standards, but must conform to the basic safety standards of BS EN 60529. So far, four supplementary letters have been agreed.

It is important to note that if the IP code does not contain the letters S or M then the protection is all embracing and is available whether or not the equipment is stationary or in motion.

H   High voltage apparatus

M   Tested against the ingress of water having harmful effects when the moving parts of the equipment are in motion.

S   Tested against the ingress of water having harmful effects when the moving parts of the equipment are stationary.

W   Suitable with specified weather conditions and provided with additional protection for such conditions.

Using the IP code

The letters IP can be followed by either two or three numerals, with or without additional letters and/or supplementary letters. Each numeral indicating the degree of protection either required or provided, any additional letter indicating the additional protection provided for persons with supplementary letters giving additional information.

Where a degree of protection is not specified or provided, the numeral is replaced by an "X", this means that there may be some protection, but the degree of protection is not specified, e.g. IP2X indicates that the degree of protection against the ingress of liquid is not specified. The "X" is used instead of "0" since "0" would indicate that no protection was given.

Where a degree of protection is given, then protection is generally afforded against all the lower degrees, e.g. equipment specified as having IP66 protection would indicate that it was also protected against 5, 4,3,2,1 and 0, for both first and second numerals. The exception is for IPX7 and IPX8 which do not indicate protection against the lower degrees of protection.

When the degree of protection against impact is agreed and BS EN 60529 is amended then the IP code will be expressed with three numerals e.g. IP 243 which indicates:

IP 2	First characteristic numeral
IP§ 4	Second characteristic numeral
IP§ § 3	Third characteristic numeral (Not given in BS EN 60529.)
IP§§§D	Additional letter
IP§§§§M	Supplementary letter
IP243DM	The above in code form.

In the above example the numerals and letters convey the following information:

2. Persons are protected against access to dangerous parts with their fingers.

    Solid foreign bodies having a diameter of 12.5 mm or larger are stopped from entering the enclosure.

4. The enclosure will not suffer any harmful effects by water being splashed at it from any direction.

3. The equipment will withstand an impact energy of 0.5 joules, which is 250 gram from a height of 200 mm.

D. Protects persons handling wires with a diameter of 1.0 mm or larger and a maximum length of 100 mm from touching dangerous parts even if the wire penetrates up to its maximum length.

M. No harmful effects due to the ingress of water when the rotating parts of the machine are moving.

    This implies that protection is not available when the equipment's moving parts are stationary. If it did the letter M would be omitted from the code.

Chapter 11

Maintenance

Types of maintenance and regulations involved

Every factory, public service building and commercial premise needs maintaining; the maintenance that has to be carried out can be broken down into four items.

1. Maintenance of the electrical system.
2. Maintenance of the premises and its infrastructure.
3. Maintenance of the equipment used.
4. Maintenance to ensure production is continuous.

The first three items in the above list have to be carried out to comply with legislation.

Item one is concerned with the Electricity at Work Regulations and in particular Regulation 4(2).

Regulation 4(2): *As may be necessary to prevent danger, all systems shall be maintained so as to prevent, so far as is reasonably practicable, such danger.*

The maintenance of the premises and its infrastructure i.e. the emergency lighting, mechanical ventilation, lightning protection and fire alarms etc., is covered by Regulation 5 of the Workplace (Health, Safety and Welfare) Regulations (WHSWR)

Regulation 5 (WHSWR): Maintenance of workplace, and of equipment, devices and systems.

(1) *The workplace and the equipment, devices and systems to which this regulation applies shall be maintained (including cleaned as appropriate) in an efficient state, in efficient working order and in good repair.*

(2) *Where appropriate, the equipment, devices and systems to which this regulation applies shall be subject to a suitable system of maintenance.*

(3) *The equipment, devices and systems to which this regulation applies are -*

(a) *equipment and devices a fault in which is liable to result in a failure to comply with any of these Regulations; and*

(b) *mechanical ventilation systems provided pursuant to regulation 6 [of these regulations] (whether or not they include equipment or devices within sub-paragraph (a) of this paragraph).*

The equipment used at work, i.e. lathes, drilling machines, photocopiers, tea makers etc., have to be maintained to comply with Regulation 5 of the Provision and Use of Work Equipment Regulations (PUWER).

Regulation 5 (PUWER): Maintenance

(1) *Every employer shall ensure that work equipment is maintained in an efficient state, in efficient working order and in good repair.*

(2)   Every employer shall ensure that where any machinery has a maintenance log, the log is kept up to date.

As far as maintenance to keep production continuous is concerned this would involve ensuring that those parts of the electrical system that cannot cause danger are maintained properly, such as checking the electrical contacts of equipment are still sound and that limit switches etc., are functioning properly.

If any parts of the electrical system are likely to cause danger, they must be maintained to comply with the Electricity at Work Regulation 4(2).

If the electrical installation has been designed, installed and inspected properly, then you start with a safe system, but there is no time scale in the regulations, so the system must remain safe throughout its intended life.

This is the object of EAW Regulation 4(2), which calls for the system to be maintained in order to prevent danger, however, the system only needs to be maintained if danger would result if it was not maintained.

Just like EAW Regulation 4(1), this regulation has to be read in conjunction with EAW Regulations 5, 6, 7, 8, 9, 10, 11, 12, and 15, but in this case there are the additional Regulations 13, 14 and 16 to take into account.

The maintenance referred to in the EAW Regulations, the Provision and Use of Work Equipment Regulations 1998 (PUWER), and the Workplace (Health, Safety and Welfare) Regulations 1992 (WHSWR), is not concerned with the manufacturing process, or keeping production going, they are only concerned with maintaining the equipment and building infrastructure to ensure that no danger will arise. There is no reason why the various functions of maintenance of the electrical system, maintenance to keep production going, or the maintenance specified in the PUWER and WHSW Regulations, cannot be combined, and it would seem that this would be the most sensible approach.

Maintenance of the fixed electrical system

Maintenance of the electrical system includes checking that the system is still suitable for the adverse or hazardous environments to which it is subjected. Quite often new lines are introduced into a factory or equipment is rearranged into a new production layout which could change the environmental conditions or the risk of mechanical damage in that particular area. Checking that the electrical installation materials are still suitable to comply with EAW Regulation 6 is important.

Regulation 6: *Electrical equipment which may reasonably foreseeably be exposed to -*
   (a)   mechanical damage;
   (b)   the effects of the weather, natural hazards, temperature or pressure;
   (c)   the effects of wet, dirty, dusty or corrosive conditions; or
   (d)   any flammable or explosive substance, including dusts, vapours or gases, shall be of such construction or as necessary protected as to prevent, so far as is reasonably practicable, danger arising from such exposure.

Many electrical faults occur because of the failure or deterioration of the conductor's insulation so part of the maintenance of the system will include checking that the insulation of electrical equipment is still satisfactory to comply with EAW Regulation 7(a) and that the actual connections are still electrically and mechanically sound to comply with EAW Regulation 10.

Regulation 7: All conductors in a system which may give rise to danger shall either-
  (a) be suitably covered with insulating material and as necessary protected so as to prevent, so far as is reasonably practicable, danger; or
  (b) have such precautions taken in respect of them (including, where appropriate, their being suitably placed) as will prevent, so far as is reasonably practicable, danger arising from such exposure.

Regulation 10: Where necessary to prevent danger, every joint and connection in a system shall be mechanically and electrically suitable for use.

In practice this means checking the insulation at terminations. The majority of circuit conductors have a single copper core covered in PVC insulation. This PVC insulation tends to creep back along the core after installation, owing to the heat generated in the conductor, exposing the live conductors at the connections thus creating a safety risk. Additionally, the constant expansion and contraction of the cables and the mechanical joint, tends with time, to loosen the connections; checking the tightness of connections is also a requirement to comply with the regulations.

Many factories have overhead cranes where the electricity supply conductors are installed below the crane track (known as down shop leads); the electrical supply to the crane being through collectors. In new factories these "down shop leads" are insulated with just a gap on the underside for the collector. In older factories these "down shop leads" are bare. They comply with EAW Regulation 7(b) since they are suitably placed, but precautions have to be taken to ensure that persons cannot come into contact with them whilst working below them, or gaining access to the crane cab, or when carrying out maintenance. Another example of EAW Regulation 7(b) is the overhead wiring between buildings. Compliance with EAW Regulation 7(b) also means ensuring that barriers and warning notices have not been removed.

Earthing system

Maintenance of the system for compliance with EAW Regulation 4(2) also means checking that the earthing of the equipment is still sound to comply with EAW Regulation 8.

Regulation 8 : Precautions shall be taken, either by earthing or by other suitable means, to prevent danger arising when any conductor (other than a circuit conductor) which may reasonably foreseeably become charged as a result of either the use of a system, or a fault in a system, becomes so charged; and, for the purposes of ensuring compliance with this regulation, a conductor shall be regarded as earthed when it is connected to the general mass of earth by conductors of sufficient strength and current-carrying capability to discharge electrical energy to earth. Ensuring that the earthing is still satisfactory is essential, since this item is relied upon to ensure that the metalwork of equipment (exposed conductive parts) do not stay charged under fault conditions, thus reducing the risk of electric shock from indirect contact.

Fuses and circuit breakers

Fuses and circuit breakers should also be looked at to ensure that they have not been broken and barriers are still in place and not left in the bottom of distribution boards.

Ideally some means of recording the magnitude and number of short-circuit currents that MCCBs have been subjected to is required, since the ultimate breaking capacity I_{cu} of BS EN 60947-2 test is O- t - CO (open - time interval - close/open) at the rated breaking capacity of the breaker. This means that the breaker is only tested to open the short-circuit current twice at its rated breaking capacity. The service rating breaking capacity I_{cs} of the MCCB is usually a percentage of the I_{cu}, (usually 50%), but the I_{cs} test is 0-t-CO-t-CO (open - time interval - close/open - time interval -close/ open). This means that the MCCB is only designed to open 50% of its fault rating three times. A similar situation exists with MCBs manufactured to BS EN 60898, although the I_{cs} is usually about 75% of the I_{cu}. Once the circuit breaker has performed such two operations at its rated breaking capacity in service, it should be replaced. Where the prospective short-circuit current is only 50% of the MCCBs rated breaking capacity it should be replaced after three operations at half its rated breaking capacity. Care is needed to be exercised since the I_{cs} value may vary depending upon the manufacturer. In general, fuses, MCCBs and MCBs should be replaced with identical units from the same manufacturer, unless the replacement has exactly the same characteristics. (See Appendix A for titles of British Standards.)

It is also essential to check that the protective devices installed in the various items of switchgear and distribution boards are of the correct size since the disconnection time of the circuit is altered when a different or larger rating protective device is installed. Additionally, a change in the type of protective device or its rating will affect the protection provided against overcurrents and may contravene EAW Regulation 11.

Regulation 11: *Efficient means, suitably located, shall be provided for protecting from excess of current every part of a system as may be necessary to prevent danger..* Regulation 11 is not only concerned with overloads it is also concerned with protecting the system against fault currents. Checking that the equipment still has an adequate fault rating is important. Quite often, in factory complexes, 500 kVA transformers are replaced with either 750 kVA or 1000 kVA transformers as the demand for power increases, the fault rating of the distribution system should have been checked when the change was made, but quite frequently this is overlooked.

It is a mandatory requirement of EAW Regulation 5 that the equipment used - which includes such items as isolators, starters, and distribution boards - can withstand any fault currents likely to flow in the system <u>before they are put into use</u>.

Regulation 5: *No electrical equipment shall be put into use where its strength and capability may be exceeded in such a way as may give rise to danger.*

In an installation where all the cable sizes and types are known, the maximum short-circuit current can be obtained by calculation. In older installations where over the years records have not been kept, or the information available is sketchy - particularly with commercial premises - an instrument similar to that shown on the left in Figure 11.1 can be used to find the prospective short-circuit current (PSC); whilst the instrument illustrated on the right in can be used for all the other basic tests.

Standard maintenance includes checking that the oil in transformers has not become acidic, causing deterioration of the windings and sludging of the oil, which can block the cooling tubes aggravating the deterioration. Oil in circuit breakers or starters should also be checked to ensure that it has not become contaminated and that there is not a film of dust or other matter on top of the oil which could lead to a flash over between phases.

Figure 11.1 - Metrotest PSC tester on left with 8-in-1 test station on right

Proving maintenance has been carried out

Although it is not a requirement of the regulations, the only way it can be proved that EAW Regulation 4(2) has been complied with is to keep records of the maintenance carried out and the test results obtained. These records should then be used to monitor that the maintenance has been effective. To keep proper records does mean identifying all fixed equipment such as, switchgear, distribution boards and cables.

Plant maintenance

As mentioned at the beginning of this chapter the various forms of maintenance required can be integrated into a single maintenance routine, with specialised items being maintained within definite time periods. Undertaking maintenance often involves opening equipment and this involves complying with the stringent requirements of EAW Regulation 14. The HSE regard this as an important regulation and will critically examine all claims that live working is necessary.

Regulation 14: No person shall be engaged in any work activity on or so near any live conductor (other than one suitably covered with insulating material so as to prevent danger) that danger may arise unless -

(a) it is unreasonable in all the circumstances for it to be dead; and

(b) it is reasonable in all the circumstances for him to be at work on or near it while it is live; and

(c) suitable precautions (including where necessary the provision of suitable protective equipment) are taken to prevent injury.

The aim of this Regulation is to strictly limit live working, it does not prevent live working, but items (a), (b) and (c) must be complied with before live working is permitted. To comply with item (c), where live working has to be undertaken, the person who is to work on live equipment must be properly trained and competent for such work.

Suitable barriers, protective clothing and test instruments complying with EAW Regulation 4 (4) will also be required, depending upon the type of live working being carried out. On high voltage equipment it would also entail ensuring that all other supplies that did not need to be live were isolated, earthed and locked in that position to comply with EAW Regulations 12 and 13 and that warning notices were displayed at the appropriate points.

Regulation 4(4): (EAWR) Any equipment provided under these Regulations for the purpose of protecting persons at work on or near electrical equipment shall be suitable for the use for which it is provided, be maintained in a condition suitable for that use, and be properly used.

This regulation is further reinforced by Regulation 4 of the Provision and Use of Equipment Regulations (PUWER).

Regulation 4 *(PUWER)* : *Suitability of work equipment*

  (1) *Every employer shall ensure that work equipment is so constructed or adapted as to be suitable for the purpose for which it is used or provided.*

  (2) *In selecting work equipment, every employer shall have regard to the working conditions and to the risks to the health and safety of persons which exist in the premises or undertaking in which that work equipment is to be used and any additional risk posed by the use of that work equipment.*

  (3) *Every employer shall ensure that work equipment is used only for operations for which, and under conditions for which, it is suitable.*

  (4) *In this regulation "suitable" means suitable in any respect which it is reasonably foreseeable will affect the health or safety of any person.*

This means that live working should only be undertaken with the authority of senior personnel who, when authorising the work to be done, must ensure that precautions have been taken such as: insulating live parts that are not going to be worked on, by screening earthed metal with insulating material, by ensuring that personnel have been trained for live working, and that persons are competent in accordance with EAW Regulation 16, and that suitable test instruments and protective clothing are provided.

The precautions taken must prevent injury. This is an absolute requirement subject only to the Regulation 29 defence. In practice, if injury results it will almost inevitably mean the regulations haver been broken.

Regulation 16: *No person shall be engaged in any work activity where technical knowledge or experience is necessary to prevent danger or, where appropriate, injury, unless he possesses such knowledge or experience, or is under such degree of supervision as may be appropriate having regard to the nature of the work.*

This regulation deals with competence which will be dealt with in a later chapter.

Although training was mentioned in Chapter two under the HSW Act it is now being specifically brought into new legislation. The following two Regulations from the PUWE Regulations illustrate the importance of providing information, instructions and training to comply with the law.

Regulation 8 *(PUWER):* *Information and instructions*

  (1) *Every employer shall ensure that all persons who use work equipment have available to them adequate health and safety information and, where appropriate, written instructions pertaining to the use of the work equipment.*

  (2) *Every employer shall ensure that any of his employees who supervises or manages the use of work equipment has available to him adequate health and safety information and, where appropriate, written instructions pertaining to the use of the work equipment.*

  (3) *Without prejudice to the generality of paragraphs (1) or (2), the information and instructions required by either of those paragraphs shall include information and, where appropriate, written instructions on-*

(a) the conditions in which and the methods by which the work equipment may be used;

(b) foreseeable abnormal situations and the action to be taken if such a situation were to occur; and

(c) any conclusions to be drawn from experience in using the work equipment.

(4) Information and instructions required by this regulation shall be readily comprehensible to those concerned.

Regulation 9 (PUWER): Training

(1) Every employer shall ensure that all persons who use work equipment have received adequate training for purposes of health and safety, including training in the methods which may be adopted when using the work equipment, any risks which such use may entail and precautions to be taken.

(2) Every employer shall ensure that any of his employees who supervises or manages the use of work equipment has received adequate training for purposes of health and safety, including training in the methods which may be adopted when using the work equipment, any risks which such use may entail and precautions to be taken.

Additionally, Regulation 12 of the PUWE Regulations covers protection against specified hazards such as; rupture or disintegration of parts of equipment, work equipment catching fire or overheating and the unintended or premature explosion of the work equipment or any article or substance produced or stored in it.

Adequate working space

When designing, installing or checking out an installation to ensure it complies with the EAW Regulations, Regulation 15 has to be taken into account.

Regulation 15: *For the purposes of enabling injury to be prevented, adequate working space, adequate means of access, and adequate lighting shall be provided at all electrical equipment on which or near which work is being done in circumstances which may give rise to danger.*

Regulation 15 does not qualify what is adequate, so the only solution is to use previous legislation, or British Standards as a guide to what is adequate. It could be argued that the space required by Regulation 17 of the Electricity (Factories Act) Special Regulations of 1908 and 1944, having been suitable for over 80 years, is still a reasonable space to allow.

British Standards can also be used as a guide, BS 5655 Part 1 for lifts (See Appendix A) gives the dimensions in a lift motor room for the space in front of the switchgear, the dimension D in Figure 10.2, being the minimum allowed from any projections on the panel front. The dimensions specified are given in Figure 10.2 along with those of Regulation 17. As far as Regulation 17 is concerned it must be remembered that the type of switchgear in use now is different from that employed 80 years ago, the depth should therefore be increased where the equipment is either withdrawable or partially withdrawable from the main switchgear housing.

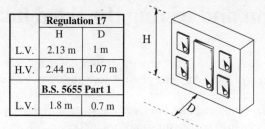

	Regulation 17	
	H	D
L.V.	2.13 m	1 m
H.V.	2.44 m	1.07 m
	B.S. 5655 Part 1	
L.V.	1.8 m	0.7 m

Figure 11.2 - Adequate working space

The width allowed should be at least that of the equipment; the minimum specified for the lift motor room being 0.5 metre. With regard to access BS 5655 also gives dimensions of the access to the lift motor room, so this could be used as a guide to the minimum allowed. As far as adequate lighting is concerned the Health and Safety Executive publish guide number HS/G 38. 'Lighting at work', which gives some guidance on this subject. Regulation 21 of the PUWE Regulations also specifies that suitable and sufficient lighting is provided, but in this case it does specify that the amount of lighting provided must take into account the operations to be carried out with the work equipment.

Lighting should be permanent, but where this is not possible, local temporary lighting can be used, care is, however, required so that the temporary lighting does not in itself create a hazard by persons tripping over leads etc.

Inspection and testing

Maintenance will require an inspection and test to be carried out to comply with the EAW Regulations. This is the subject of the next chapter.

Portable appliances

Items that may be connected to the system will require maintenance, particularly portable appliances, which are covered in detail in Chapter 13.

Isolation

To enable maintenance to be carried out, suitable means have to be provided to cut off the electrical supplies to any electrical equipment. Isolation is the subject of the EAW and the PUWE Regulations and is covered in more detail in Chapter 14.

Chapter 12

Inspection and testing the fixed installation

The periods between carrying out the various items of maintenance discussed in the previous chapter will vary. At some point in time, tests, as well as inspection of the system, will be required. Where the installation is recently new, it is a relatively simple task to keep track of alterations to the system as they occur, but where the installation has been in existence for some time and records of modifications have not been kept, then a more detailed investigation is required.

Whether the installation is new or old it pays to approach the problem in a logical manner. The first requirement is to identify the system and the equipment, both fixed and portable, connected to it.

System parameters

Identifying the system includes identifying the parameters associated with the electrical supply to the premises as given in the following list.

1. Maximum demand of the installation.
2. Number and types of live conductors of the supply.
3. Type of earthing arrangement.
4. Nature of current and frequency.
5. Prospective short-circuit current at the origin of the installation.
6. Size and type of protective device at the origin.
7. Phase earth loop impedance external to the installation.

The maximum demand of an installation is the amount of electrical power required at any particular time and is usually expressed as an electrical-current demand which takes into account any diversity. The supply to the premises will have been based on a stated maximum demand when the supply was first given. However, as the business expands more load is usually added to the existing demand. A check should have been made to ensure the distribution switchgear and cables were suitable for the increased demand; quite often this is not done.

It will also be necessary to identify the cable impedances in each part of the distribution system. Since the maximum fault current is only limited by the phase impedance, installing larger distribution cables to cater for the increase in load allows a higher fault level to appear further into the distribution system. Again a check should have been made to ensure that the equipment is suitable for this increase in fault level.

If there are no drawings of the distribution system then a line drawing should be produced, similar to that shown in figure 12.1, so that switchgear, distribution board and cable sizes can be recorded. The cable impedances can also be recorded at each distribution point.

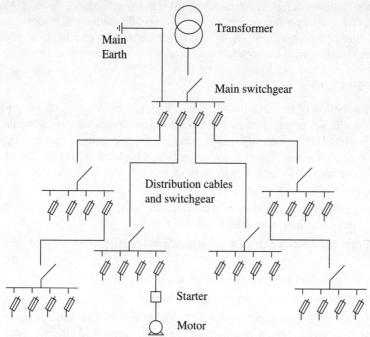

Fig 12.1 - System Distribution

The maximum demand load can be determined for each distribution point and recorded, as can: the voltage at each point, the maximum and minimum fault currents at each point and the earth loop impedance at each point. In determining the maximum demand at each distribution point the load on final circuits will also have been determined.

Having obtained the necessary information it is now possible to start to check: that the cables are correctly sized for the likely load and prospective fault currents, that the protective devices installed are of the correct type and rating for the circuits concerned, that the voltage at equipment is as required by British Standards or suitable for the safe functioning of equipment and that where required the circuits will disconnect in the appropriate time to give protection against indirect contact.

The next stage is a physical inspection of the installation to ensure that the equipment used is suitable for the applicable environmental conditions as spelt out by EAW Regulation 6, to confirm that corrosion or mechanical damage has not subsequently occurred in the installation and that there is sufficient working space, access and lighting to enable maintenance to be carried out so that EAW Regulation 15 is complied with. The inspection would also cover checking that isolators and emergency stop buttons have been suitably placed in accordance with EAW Regulation 12. It is also important to check that personnel do not have to remove and replace fuses, circuit breakers, etc., near live conductors; this can happen when instruments are installed in cubicles and when standby generators are used.

Physical inspection

The physical inspection of the installation would include checking all those items mentioned in the chapter on maintenance. Also that joints in conduits, trunking and armoured cables have been correctly made to ensure earth continuity, since slight defects in these items will not show up when the circuit is tested. Other items to be incorporated in the physical check would include:

1. That connections are tight.
2. That equipment has been manufactured to British Standards, or the Harmonised European equivalent.
3. That equipment doors are fixed properly and not held in place by bits of string etc.
4. That every circuit is provided with a means of isolation.
5. That all removable barriers have been replaced.
6. That labels identifying the purpose of switchgear, control gear and emergency stopping devices have been installed, where confusion would otherwise exist as to which item controlled the equipment.
7. That warning notices have been fixed where the voltage exceeds 250 volts in equipment where it would not normally be expected to exist.
8. That additional holes have not been made in the equipment, or if they have, that they have been properly blanked off.
9. That flexible conduit connections to equipment are not damaged and that the protective conductor connection across the flexible connection is in place and in good condition.

In hazardous areas additional checks will have to be made, some of which are listed below.

1. That the equipment installed is suitable for the zone of risk in which it is installed and that it has the correct temperature classification for the ignition temperature of the gasses or vapours present.
2. That any glasses or glass-metal seals are satisfactory.

3. That all bolts are tight and no bolts are missing.
4. The equipment is protected against corrosion and vibration.
5. That stopper boxes are in place and filled with the correct compound.
6. That the equipment is protected against any other environmental conditions as outlined in EAW Regulation 6 and complies with the appropriate IP code classification.

Tests to be carried out

Having completed a physical check of the installation, tests can now to be carried out to check the continuity of live and protective conductors and to verify that there will be no tracking between live conductors or live conductors and earth, and that the circuit will be disconnected fast enough to reduce the risk of persons receiving an electric shock by indirect contact.

The following tests should be carried out:
1. Continuity of equipotential bonding conductors, supplementary equipotential bonding conductors and protective conductors.
2. Continuity of live conductors, which includes the neutral.
3. The resistance of earth electrodes.
4. Insulation resistance of all live conductors to earth.
5. Insulation resistance between live conductors.
6. Polarity to ensure all switches are connected in phase conductors and not neutral. (Should only apply to new work.)
7. Phase earth loop impedance measurements.
8. Operation of residual current devices.

There are two requirements for carrying out the tests on the installation; the first is the correct instruments and the second is a competent person. (See page 118.)

Regulation 16: *(EAWR) No person shall be engaged in any work activity where technical knowledge or experience is necessary to prevent danger or, where appropriate, injury, unless he possesses such knowledge or experience, or is under such degree of supervision as may be appropriate having regard to the nature of the work.*

This means that the person carrying out the tests must be familiar with the instruments he is going to use and has been trained in how to use them and knows how to interpret the test results. In general, this means using a qualified electrician.

Interpretation of the results is important since it is easy for a circuit to be accepted when in fact it should fail. This is particularly true with the phase earth loop impedance test results. The installation should have been designed so that the disconnection time for protection against indirect contact is determined with the resistance of the conductors being at the temperature they will reach with the fault current flowing. The tests will be carried out at a different temperature and the results will therefore require adjusting to the design temperature or, the design values of Z (or R) from the tables will require adjusting to the temperature at the time of test.

Where the final circuit is at the end of a distribution scheme similar to that shown in Figure 12.1, the fault current will probably be insufficient to raise the distribution cables up to the design temperature of those cables. However, since the object is to prove the circuit is safe, assuming that the distribution cables are raised to their design temperature introduces a safety factor and at the same time makes the interpretation of the test results easier. If the test result at the end of a distribution scheme was on the borderline, in practice, it could be accepted due to the feeder cables not being raised to their design temperature.

Figure 12.2 gives a typical table from the *Handbook on the IEE Wiring Regulations - BS 7671- by the author* where the protective conductor is made from the same type of material as the phase conductor. This shows how the earth loop impedance values need to be reduced for the difference between the temperature at the time the tests are carried out and the temperature used for designing the circuit.

Some form of record is required of tests and checks carried out, if only to ensure that the same area of the premises is not checked each time to the exclusion of the rest of the premises. This can be achieved by having a test schedule similar to Figure 12.3 which records the tests and checks made at the distribution board. The same form could easily be adapted to cover switchgear. It also enables circuit parameters to be recorded so that time is not wasted finding them out the next time a test is carried out. Spotting deterioration between successive test readings enables preventative maintenance to be carried out.

Instruments and systems of work

Inspection, testing and maintenance cannot be carried out properly unless the necessary instruments are available, although the instruments required will depend upon the type of electrical equipment and the type of maintenance to be carried out. The following is a list of the basic instruments required for a mains voltage installation.

Insulation tester minimum voltage 500 volt.

Phase earth loop impedance tester.

RCD tester.

Continuity tester.

Polarity tester.

Portable appliance tester.

Earth resistance tester (if earth electrodes are installed).

SHOCK PROTECTION   ZS 1A   BS 88 HRC FUSES

Maximum design & testing values of earth loop impedance Z_S for BS 88 Part 2.2 fuses when U_0 is 240V

DISCONNECTION TIME 5 SECONDS

Maximum values of Z_S in ohms for different HRC fuse sizes

Temperature degrees C	2	4	6	10	16	20	25	32	40	50	63	80	100	125	160	200	250	315	400	500
										Maximum value of Z_S in ohms										
Design	47	23	14.1	7.74	4.36	3.04	2.4	1.92	1.41	1.09	0.86	0.6	0.44	0.35	0.27	0.2	0.16	0.12	0.09	0.065
Testing	For testing the following maximum values of Z_S are based on a design temperature of 115 °C																			
30	35.1	17.2	10.52	5.78	3.25	2.27	1.79	1.43	1.05	0.81	0.64	0.448	0.328	0.261	0.201	0.149	0.122	0.087	0.067	0.049
25	34.6	16.9	10.37	5.69	3.21	2.24	1.76	1.41	1.04	0.80	0.63	0.441	0.324	0.257	0.199	0.147	0.120	0.086	0.066	0.048
20	34.1	16.7	10.22	5.61	3.16	2.20	1.74	1.39	1.02	0.79	0.62	0.435	0.319	0.254	0.196	0.145	0.118	0.085	0.065	0.047
15	33.6	16.4	10.07	5.53	3.11	2.17	1.71	1.37	1.01	0.78	0.61	0.429	0.314	0.250	0.193	0.143	0.116	0.084	0.064	0.046
10	33.1	16.2	9.93	5.45	3.07	2.14	1.69	1.35	0.99	0.77	0.61	0.423	0.310	0.246	0.190	0.141	0.115	0.082	0.063	0.046
5	32.6	16.0	9.79	5.38	3.03	2.11	1.67	1.33	0.98	0.76	0.60	0.417	0.306	0.243	0.188	0.139	0.113	0.081	0.063	0.045
0	32.2	15.8	9.66	5.30	2.99	2.08	1.64	1.32	0.97	0.75	0.59	0.411	0.301	0.240	0.185	0.137	0.112	0.080	0.062	0.045
-5	31.8	15.5	9.53	5.23	2.95	2.05	1.62	1.30	0.95	0.74	0.58	0.405	0.297	0.236	0.182	0.135	0.110	0.079	0.061	0.044

Notes: The above values for testing are based on the phase and cpc conductors, both being copper or aluminium. Calculations are based on the resistance-temperature coefficient of 0.004 per °C at 20 °C.

Where the voltage to earth is not 240V, multiply the Z_S from the table by the actual voltage to earth, and then divide by 240V, to give the revised Z_S value for the actual voltage to earth.

Figure 12.2 - Earth loop impedance from the *Handbook on the IEE Wiring Regulations BS 7671* by Trevor E. Marks

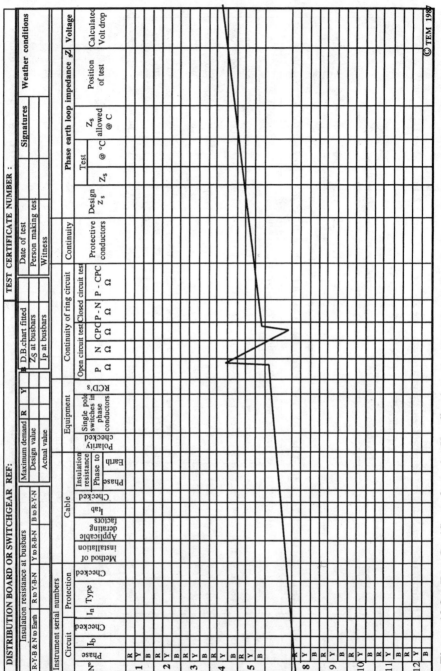

Figure 12.3 - Test Certificate from the *Handbook on the IEE Wiring Regulations - BS7671* by Trevor E. Marks

Details of tests

The insulation test is made to establish that there is no deterioration in the insulation value of the conductors. These tests can, however, only be carried out when the electricity is switched off, which may mean testing when the premises are closed.

The first test is between all the live conductors and earth. This can be carried out at the mains position by strapping all the live conductors together and then testing to earth. When testing at the mains position it is essential for all the distribution and final circuits to be switched on. If the test result is satisfactory there is no need to test at each individual board. However, if a poor reading is obtained, which could be the case in a large installation, the installation is broken down into smaller sections for testing and each section is tested to prove that it is satisfactory or to find the circuit that requires attention.

The second test is a little more complicated since it involves switching out of circuit those items where there is a connection between phase and neutral or between phases. The test is then made between each live conductor as shown in the following table.

Conductor	Test Between Conductors connected together
Red phase	Yellow & Blue phases and Neutral
Yellow phase	Red & Blue phases & Neutral
Blue phase	Red & Yellow phases & Neutral
Neutral	Red, Yellow & Blue phases

The insulation resistance test instrument must be capable of passing a current of 1 mA at the test voltage when the insulation resistance is the minimum allowed for the type of circuit being tested. The accuracy of the instrument need not exceed 2 per cent full scale deflection. The test voltage and the minimum insulation resistance allowed is given below.

Extra-low voltage circuits (0 - 50 V a.c or 120 V d.c)

Supplied from an isolating transformer to BS 3535. Test voltage 250 V d.c. Minimum insulation resistance 0.25 megohm.

Low voltage up to 500 V (50 V to 500 V a.c.)

Test voltage 500 V d.c. Minimum insulation resistance 0.5 megohm.

Low voltage between 500 V and 1000 V

Test voltage 1000 V d.c. Minimum insulation resistance 1 megohm.

The phase earth loop impedance tests are made at the end of final circuits and the readings obtained being adjusted for the temperature at which the tests were made. The adjusted readings are then compared with the maximum allowed for the type and rating of the circuit's protective device.

A typical RCD Tester, illustrated in Figure 12.4, tests between the phase and protective conductor. The loads normally supplied through the RCD are disconnected during the test, the test being made on the load side of the RCD. The tests to be applied will depend upon the Standard to which the RCD was manufactured. For RCDs manufactured to BS 4293 two tests are made, one at 50% of the operating current $I_{\Delta n}$ and the other at its operating current. In the first test the RCD should not trip and in the second it should trip within 200 ms (0.2s). Where the RCD is used as supplementary protection against direct contact the second test is made with a test current of 150 mA and the RCD should trip within 40 ms (0.04s) and the test period must not exceed 50 ms.

For safety reasons, and before any tests are carried out, the circuits must first have the phase earth loop impedance checked to ensure that, for general installations, the product of earth loop impedance Z_s multiplied by the operating current of the RCD $I_{\Delta n}$ does not exceed 50 V. This is important since an open circuit on the protective conductor would cause the installation's exposed conductive parts to rise to mains potential when the RCD test was made.

The test button on the RCD must then be operated before any tests are carried out to prove that the RCD functions properly. It must also be operated after the tests have been carried out to prove the RCD is still functional. The test button on the RCD should be operated every three months. The test period for the RCD test will depend upon the environmental conditions. In clean, dry, dust free atmospheres where the RCD is not going to be damaged, testing every five years should be sufficient if the test button is used every three months.

The continuity test is made with a low resistance ohmmeter, but should not be required in an existing installation where the continuity has previously been proved. It will be required for new work or alterations and, or extensions that have been carried out. If this test is required it should be carried out before any other tests. The instrument should have a minimum test current of 200 mA with an open circuit voltage between 4 and 24 V.

Polarity can be checked by using a continuity tester (with the electricity off) or when carrying out earth loop impedance or RCD tests, since these instruments usually check polarity and give a warning not to proceed if the polarity is wrong. Testing portable appliances is covered in a separate chapter, which will also give the period between tests.

A typical Earth Resistance Tester is illustrated in Figure 12.5 and is only required where the installation has had its own earth rods installed for example, if the installation takes its supply from a transformer or the electricity supply company cannot provide an earth and the system used is a TT system. (Details of this test are given in the *Handbook on the IEE Wiring Regulations - BS7671,* for those who are interested in this test.)

Where instruments having a multi-range of voltages and amperes are used for plant maintenance they must be equipped with fusible leads.

Where instruments are used for testing circuits in a hazardous area they should be intrinsically safe and suitable for the explosive liquids, solids or gasses in the area

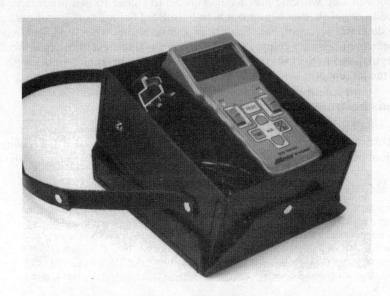

Figure 12.4 - Metrotest M1600 digital RCD with d.c. test

Figure 12.5 - Megger earth tester for use in finding earth rod resistance

where testing is being carried out.

A code of safe working practice is required to enable formal procedures to be adopted to establish; that equipment is fully isolated before work commences, that wiring diagrams are available, that the proper instruments are used and that they have been maintained to comply with Regulation 4(4) of the Electricity at Work Act and Regulation 5 of the Provision and Use of Work Equipment Regulations given in full in the last chapter.

Periods between inspections

The Institution of Electrical Engineers has collated the various recommendations from British Standards and other organisations and produced a list giving the maximum periods between inspecting and testing a fixed low voltage installation.

General Installation

Domestic	Change of occupancy/10years
Commercial	Change of occupancy/ 5years
Educational establishments	5 years
Hospitals	5 years
Industrial	3 years
Residential accommodation	5 years
Offices	5 years
Shops	5 years
Laboratories	5 years

Buildings open to the public

Cinemas	3 years
Church installations	5 years
Leisure Complexes (excluding swimming pools)	3 years
Places of public entertainment	3 years
Restaurants and Hotels	5 years
Theatres	3 years
Public Houses	5 years
Village halls/Community centres	5 years

Special installations

Agricultural and horticultural	3 years
Caravans	3 years
Caravan parks	1 year
Highway power supplies	6 years
Marinas	1 year
Fish farms	1 year
Swimming pools	1 year
Emergency lighting	3 years
Fire alarms	1 year
Launderettes	1 year
Petrol filling stations	1 year
Construction site installations	3 months

Chapter 13

Portable equipment

Two definitions bring portable and transportable electrical equipment within the scope of the regulations. The first definition is that of a system and the second is that of electrical equipment.

System: means an electrical system in which all the electrical equipment is, or may be, electrically connected to a common source of electrical energy, and includes such source and such equipment.

Electrical equipment: includes anything used, intended to be used or installed for use, to generate, provide, transmit, transform, rectify, convert, conduct, distribute, control, store, measure or use electrical energy.

The important words in the definition of system are 'or may be', and in the definition of electrical equipment are 'includes anything used, intended to be used'. This means any item of electrical equipment on the premises, whether it is being used or not. And since from the above definitions any item of electrical equipment is part of the system, any equipment on the premises has to be maintained to ensure that danger will not arise. This does not, of course, apply to spares on the stores shelf, or to items of equipment that have been rendered unusable whilst they are waiting to be repaired.

Regulation 4(1): (EAWR) All systems shall at all times be of such construction as to prevent, so far as is reasonably practicable, danger.

Regulation 4(2): (EAWR) As may be necessary to prevent danger, all systems shall be maintained so as to prevent, so far as is reasonably practicable, such danger.

As can be seen from Regulations 4(1) and (2), the emphasis is on the word "system" which has already been defined. The word system could be replaced by the words "electrical equipment" which makes the regulation's requirements clearer.

Portable equipment defined

So far the book has only dealt with the fixed installation, but the regulations are applicable to portable equipment and transportable equipment as well. The words "portable equipment" include all items that are connected to the electrical supply through a flexible cable or cord and plug. Portable equipment can be subdivided into items that can be easily moved from room to room (i.e. electric fan heaters, electric typewriters etc.) and hand-held equipment which is held in the hand whilst it is being used; the most obvious items of hand-held equipment are: electric drills, vacuum cleaners and hand lamps. The word "transportable" has been introduced to cover those items of equipment that can be moved and receive their electrical supply through a cable or lead which is permanently connected to the fixed installation. The equipment can still be moved, either because the equipment is light enough or it is on wheels or rollers. An example is a large photocopier or a high pressure water washer.

This distinction between the fixed installation and portable or transportable equipment is important, since items that are held in the hand whilst they are being used or are still energised whilst they are being moved, pose a greater danger than the fixed installation because the cable leads and plug tops are more prone to damage. The pulling of leads tight because they are not quite long enough to reach the point the portable, or transportable, item is required to function, puts a tremendous strain on the connections into the equipment and on those in the plug top.

Types of equipment

There are three basic types of construction of equipment to protect against electric shock; these are Class I, Class II and Class III.

Class I: the electrical components have at least functional insulation throughout to enable them to work and are provided with an earthing terminal. Equipment which is designed to be connected by flexible lead or cord is either provided with an earthing contact at the inlet or the lead is non-detachable.

A protective conductor (earth) must connect a Class I appliance to the main earth terminal of the installation.

Note: it is possible for Class 1 equipment to have external casings or accessible parts that are non-conductive or are separated from hazardous voltages by double or reinforced insulation, for example desktop computers.

Class II: the appliance is either double insulated or has reinforced insulation throughout and no provision is made for earthing. The appliance is so designed that if there are any external metal parts they will not become live in the event of a fault in the appliance.

A protective conductor (earth) must not be connected to a Class II appliance, which can be identified, as mentioned in Chapter 4, by the following sign.

Figure 13.1- Class II symbol

Class III: the protection against electric shock relies on the voltage not exceeding 50 V a.c. or 120 V ripple free d.c. and the electrical supply complies with the requirements for SELV (used to be called Safety Extra-low Voltages but now referred to as Seperated Extra-low voltage). Additionally, a voltage higher than those given above are not generated within the equipment.

The plug of Class III equipment must only fit into a socket outlet designated for the Class III supply and it must not fit into any other type of socket outlet.

This means that a nonstandard plug and socket-outlet must be used for the Class III supply.

The live parts of SELV circuits must not be connected to earth, to protective conductors, or live parts of other circuits. The source of the SELV supply must be through an isolation transformer manufactured to BS 3535 when connected to the mains, or have equivalent insulation between windings etc., when connected to a generator or other source used for the supply. A battery or other source independent of higher voltage can be used.

A protective conductor must not be connected to a Class III appliance, which can be identified by the following sign.

Figure 13.2 - Class III symbol

Selection for use

The first requirement for any employer or self employed person is to check that the equipment he is going to use is suitable for the work intended to be carried out. This is a requirement of the Provision and Use of Work Equipment Regulations (PUWER), which will be covered more fully in the chapter on Work Activity. In selecting the correct equipment to be used account must be taken of the environmental conditions spelled out in EAW Regulation 6.

Regulation 6: *Electrical equipment which may reasonably foreseeably be exposed to -*

(a) mechanical damage;

(b) the effects of the weather, natural hazards, temperature or pressure;

(c) the effects of wet, dirty, dusty or corrosive conditions; or

(d) any flammable or explosive substance, including dusts, vapours or gases,

shall be of such construction or as necessary protected as to prevent, so far as is reasonably practicable, danger arising from such exposure.

This is particularly important where equipment is used outside. Quite often non-weatherproof materials such as domestic type socket-outlets mounted on a wooden pattress are used outside when it is fine and dry, but are not brought inside when it starts to drizzle with rain, thereby increasing the risk of electric shock. Such arrangements should not be allowed and proper extension leads should be used with weatherproof BS EN 60309 (BS 4343) socket outlets and plug tops. It is dangerous and wrong to expect anyone to behave in a reasonable manner. The attitude "It will be all right, it will only take me five minutes to do it." is still very prevalent and is no excuse if an accident occurs.

Maintenance

It has already been established that maintenance has to be carried out. The problem for most persons is - what maintenance has to be carried out, how often should it be carried out and who can carry it out? The answers to these questions will be covered in this chapter.

The amount of maintenance and the frequency that it has to be carried out depends upon: the environmental conditions (EAW Regulation 6), the location where the equipment is to be used, the type of equipment, the age of the equipment, the existing state of the equipment, how often the equipment will be used and how much abuse the equipment is likely to receive. Once a maintenance system has been set up, analysis of the maintenance records to see the type and number of repairs will determine the frequency of maintenance required. Analysis of the maintenance record will also show which items of equipment are being abused, in order that remedial action can be taken.

The maintenance of portable equipment breaks down into two functions; the first is an inspection and the second is testing. The frequency of inspection is greater than the frequency of tests.

Who can carry out the maintenance ?

The Regulations state that a person must be competent:

Regulation 16: *(EAWR) No person shall be engaged in any work activity where technical knowledge or experience is necessary to prevent danger or, where appropriate, injury, unless he possesses such knowledge or experience, or is under such degree of supervision as may be appropriate having regard to the nature of the work.*

All that being competent means is that persons must have been trained for the work to be undertaken, by knowing what to look for, what to do and have sufficient knowledge of the work function to enable them to avoid danger to themselves or other persons. It is, therefore, possible to categorise competency.

Category I competency

In its simplest form, this means that a person need not be skilled in electrical work, but trained to inspect certain types of equipment and carry out routine tests with a PASS/FAIL indicating type of instrument.

Category II competency

Where the equipment is more complex or the instruments give readings that need interpretation the person should be skilled in electrical work. More formal training is required to interpret the instrument readings properly and the actions that need to be taken depending upon the test results. This person becomes competent by technical knowledge and experience.

Offices, hotels, small shops and small companies

Since 95% of the faults with portable equipment can be detected by inspection it is a relatively simple matter to train someone to undertake this work. In offices, hotels, small shops and small companies, where the equipment used is standard and not hi-tech, a member of the staff can be trained to carry out the inspection and testing of the portable equipment using a PASS/FAIL indicating instrument.

Large commercial or public premises and factories

In large commercial or public premises, factories and larger companies where a whole range of portable or hi-tech equipment is used, the degree of competency should be category II.

All organisations - especially the small ones

The user of the equipment should also be taught how to inspect the equipment before they use it. They should be instructed not to use any equipment that fails the visual inspection, and to report any defects to the management immediately.

How often should maintenance be carried out?

It is the duty holder's responsibility to determine the frequency of inspecting the equipment and the period between tests; the problem is knowing how often it should be done at the start. In this respect the Health and Safety Executive have been helpful by suggesting initial intervals for a formal inspection and for the combined inspection and test for different types of user. These periods can then be increased or reduced in the light of experience by analysis of the inspection and test results. The periods for inspection and testing are given in Figure 13.3.

In industrial premises or construction sites where the equipment is returned to the stores each day and then drawn from the stores the following day, the store keeper can be trained to carry out a visual inspection every time the equipment is issued and withdraw it from service when a fuller inspection and test is due. Where the equipment is issued for an indefinite period whilst a particular work function is being carried out, it should have an initial inspection and then be inspected and tested at regular intervals.

Labelling equipment

There is no requirement in the EAW Regulations to label equipment. Labelling equipment is, therefore, a management procedure. It is the only way that a user of

Portable Appliances - Periods between inspections

Type of user	Formal visual inspection	Combined inspection and testing
Construction site		
issued from stores	Before issue	3 months
issued for long period	Ditto & 1 month	3 months
Industrial		
issued from stores	Before issue	6-12 months
issued for long period	Ditto & 3 months	6-12 months
Equipment hire	Before issue	After return
Offices, hotels and tourist accommodation		
Extra-low voltage - Less than 50 V, i.e., telephone equipment, L.V. desk lights. Battery operated less than 20V	None	None
Information technology equipment Desktop computers, VDU screens, photocopiers and fax machines that are NOT hand-held and rarely moved.	2 -4 years	Not if double insulated otherwise 5 years
Double insulated equipment NOT HAND-HELD and only moved occasionally, e.g. fans, table lamps and slide projectors.	2 -4 years	None
Double insulated equipment HAND-HELD e.g. some types of vacuums and floor cleaners.	Before use and 6 months to 1 year	None
Class I (earthed) equipment - e.g. electric kettles, some floor cleaners, some kitchen equipment and irons.	Before use and 6 months to 1 year	1 - 2 years
Cables (leads and plugs for above) and mains voltage extension leads	6 months to 4 years	1 - 5 years
	Depending upon the type of office, hotel or tourist accommodation equipment, to which it is connected.	

Figure 13.3 - Initial periods between inspections

Compiled from information provided by the Health and Safety Executive.

the equipment, or the store keeper for that matter, will know that the equipment is due for an inspection and test. When suitably numbered, it also enables a record to be kept of where the equipment is and the inspection and tests carried out. Labelling of the equipment does not need to be complicated, all that is required is the date after which the equipment must not be used. Preferably the label should have the company's name on it to make it distinctive and to stop any other person just putting a label on the equipment with a different date. Unless very little electrical equipment is used each item should also be numbered.

What maintenance has to be carried out

Before any maintenance is carried out it is important for safety reasons to check equipment is disconnected from all sources of hazardous voltage, particularly Uninterruptible Power Supplies (UPS).

The most important component in any maintenance schedule is the visual inspection of equipment by a competent person at regular intervals with the tests being carried out at defined intervals. The following lists are given as a guide to what is required for inspecting the equipment for those companies who want to set up their own inspection and testing procedure.

The visual inspection consists of:

1. Checking the cable lead to ensure that:
   (a) there are no cuts in the cable lead,
   (b) any scuffing or abrasions of the cable sheath are light and it is not worn down to the cores,
   (c) there are no taped joints in the lead,
   (d) there is no sign of damage due to overheating of the lead,
   (e) that the cable lead has three cores for Class I equipment,
   (f) the cable has not been damaged by chemicals,
   (g) not been squashed by being run over, trapped between desks or stretched,
   (h) the means of disconnection or isolation from the mains supply are readily accessible,
   (i) equipment is not positioned so close to walls or partitions that the cord is forced into a tight bend as it exits from the equipment,
   (j) the equipment is located so that cords are not under tension; with technology equipment it is important that the cord does not exert an undue pull on the appliance coupler pulling it out of alignment with the fixed connector

2. Checking the plug:
   (a) that the cable sheath is firmly trapped under the clamp in the plug, i.e., the cores of the cable are not showing outside the body of the plug,

(b)   that the connections in the plug are correct i.e. brown to terminal 'L', blue to terminal 'N' and the green/yellow conductor to terminal 'E',

(c)   that there are no loose strands of conductor sticking out of the cable termination, i.e. all the cable strands are in the termination,

(d)   that the terminal screws are tight,

(e)   that the insulation on the cable core goes right up to the cable termination,

(f)   that there are no splits in the core insulation in the plug,

(g)   that there is no discoloration to the terminations, cable cores or plug pins, due to overheating,

(h)   that the plug has the correct size and type of fuse recommended by the appliance manufacturer and that it has not been repaired with fuse wire or covered with metal foil,

(i)   that the pins of the plug are not bent or distorted and the case is not broken or cracked and screws are not bent or missing,

(j)   that there has been no entry of dust, dirt, liquid or chemicals into the plug,

(k)   the plug is correct for the environmental conditions,

(l)   that the plug and cable are checked for end-to-end polarity.

3.   Checking the appliance or equipment:

(a)   the cable termination complies with the same requirements as given under 2 for the plug,

(b)   that there is no damage to the outside of the equipment that exposes live parts, terminations or, in the case of double insulated equipment, reduces the insulation value of the protecting cover,

(c)   that any switches are functioning correctly and not sticking in the ON position,

(d)   that the protective conductor connection is sound and securely fixed to the frame and metal casing of Class I equipment,

(e)   that the space around the equipment is adequate for ventilation and cooling, that equipment ventilation openings are not blocked by documents or other items,

(f)   that cups, plants or other items containing liquids are not placed where they can easily spill into equipment such as, the keyboards of computers,

(g)   that the equipment is operated with all covers in place and doors closed.

Tests to be carried out

Again the tests required for a maintenance check are simple. There are only two basic tests required to be carried out. The first is continuity of the protective conductor for

Class I equipment and the second is an insulation resistance test between the phase and neutral conductor and earth. The second test is carried out with any switches on the appliance switched on.

Many test instruments can give flash tests, load tests, operation tests and earth leakage tests. These are not necessary unless the equipment has been stripped for repair and rebuilt. They are only then applied to prove the integrity of the repaired equipment. The British Standard requires a flash test to be made at the factory as part of the appliance testing procedure before it is sold. It does not require flash tests to be carried out after the appliance has left the factory. Under no circumstances must a flash test be applied to computer equipment.

Before discussing the tests it must be pointed out that extreme care has to be exercised with computers, so the test procedure for computers will be given separately.

Inspection always precedes testing. Tests are not carried out until the appliance, its lead and its plug pass the inspection.

Carrying out the tests

Where the equipment has a metal case (exposed conductive part) then the earth connection made by the protective conductor has to be proved. This is done by testing from the earth pin of the plug to accessible metal parts on the equipment and passing a current through the protective conductor, depending upon the rating of the equipment, in accordance with Figure 13.4. The maximum resistance allowed is given in the last column. Where an appliance is connected to an extension lead, the extension lead should be included in the inspection and test. Any other extension leads on the premises should also be inspected and tested.

The next test is the insulation resistance test, which is the same for both Class I and Class II equipment. For this test the phase (L) and neutral (N) are strapped together at the plug top - this is best done by having a test socket where the L and N pins are connected together properly - and a test is made between the L and N pins and accessible metal parts of the equipment, the test and results required being shown in figure 13.4. (Note; HSE Guidance Note PM32 recommends that the earth continuity test current is not less than twice the fuse rating.)

Inspecting and testing computers

Computers can be easily damaged by tests being carried out so it is advisable to consult the manufacturer of the equipment to obtain the appropriate test data and recommended test criteria; if you are not sure how to carry out the tests seek expert advice. The EEA have produced a ten page guide for periodic safety checks of business equipment, The address of EEA is given in Appendix B.

Portable Appliances - Tests and Results Required			
Type of test	**Test voltage**	**Test current**	**Test result**
Earth bond test - Class I only			
Equipment rated up to 6 amps	12 V d.c.	12 amps	0.5 Ω Maximum
3A or 5A fuse - 0.5 sq mm cable			
Equipment rated over 6 amps	12 V d.c.	25 amps	0.1 Ω Maximum
10A or 13A fuse - larger cable			
Insulation test			
Class I equipment	500 V d.c	1 mA	2 MΩ Minimum
Class II equipment	500 V d.c	1 mA	7 MΩ Minimum
Computers			
Earth bond test - Class I only	12 V d.c.	100 mA	0.1 Ω Maximum
Preferred voltage	100 mV	100 mA	0.1 Ω Maximum
Class I - insulation test	500 V d.c.	1 mA	2 MΩ Minimum
Class II - insulation test	500 V d.c.	1 mA	7 MΩ Minimum

Figure 13.4 - Tests and results required

Some computers have a detachable power lead, in which case the lead can be inspected and tested like any other piece of equipment once it has been detached from the computer and the electricity supply.

Before any inspection and testing begins it is important to obtain permission to carry out the tests and make arrangements to have the equipment and all data links disconnected. Be especially careful with fibre optic cables, do not look into the end of the connector. The power in fibre optic cables is not obvious, the light they emit is not visible but can be very damaging to the eyes. Where fibre optic cables are clearly identified there is no need to disconnect them.

Initial inspection

Check the area where the computer is being used to ensure that the cables and plug are so located that they are not under strain or likely to be damaged. Check that the ventilation holes in the equipment are not covered up and that liquid refreshments and plant pots are not located where they can spill into the equipment or the keyboard.

Power down the equipment in accordance with the manufacturer's instructions, number and unplug all external signal cables ensuring it is safe to do so. Hazardous voltage can appear at the connector shield. Manufacturers specify using only one hand to remove the connector ensuring that the rest of the body is not in contact with earth. If extra effort is required to remove the connector use insulated pliers with the other hand. Having disconnected the cable check the connector and socket to ground (earth) for an a.c. voltage. If a voltage in excess of 10 volts is present, carefully reconnect the cables and inform the customer, head of department, or safety officer of a safety hazard and inform your Manufacturer's representative. If there are no problems, unplug the mains supply to the equipment.

With all covers in place check the exterior of the equipment for: covers fitting properly; physical damage, especially at socket outlets; switches, fuses and cables looping power between units; signs of overheating or fire damage and for signs of liquids or foreign matter entering the equipment. Inspect the power cord and plug top as listed under items one and two in the list of maintenance to be carried out.

Testing computers and IT equipment

Before doing anything make sure the equipment has been isolated from the electrical supply for at least five minutes to allow capacitors to discharge. Computers, VDUs and hard disks etc., can be contained in an insulating case but still have an earth connected to them. Where the cable lead is permanently connected to the equipment the normal continuity test is carried out between the earth pin on the plug and the metal where the cable enters the equipment. If the cable enters the equipment through an insulating plate it will be necessary to remove the cover and test to the protective conductor cable core - NOWHERE ELSE.

The continuity test using 100 mV is recommended where the equipment has exposed conductive parts. Higher voltages than this can break down surface corrosion films at loose connections and earth continuity within the equipment is often through printed circuit boards. The insulation test is carried out as for other equipment but to any exposed metal parts on the equipment.

Where a considerable number of items have to be tested it may be more convenient to use a Portable Appliance Tester (PAT) which stores the test results and allows them to be down loaded to a computer as illustrated in Figure 13.5. The computer can then be made to run the maintenance programme.

Information Technology equipment (IT) should not be subjected to electric strength testing - also known as hi-pot testing, or flash testing - because this may damage insulation.

Uninterruptible Power Systems (UPS)

These should only be tested by a Category II competent person in conjunction with the manufacturer's instructions, since they still give out power when the mains power is cut off or disconnected even if it is supplied from a socket-outlet and plug.

Testing transformers

As far as portable transformers i.e., those that are used with portable tools, are concerned, the lead and plug can be inspected and tested as already outlined in this chapter. With the unit disconnected the connections on the output sockets and any internal fuses should be checked. There should be an earthed screen between

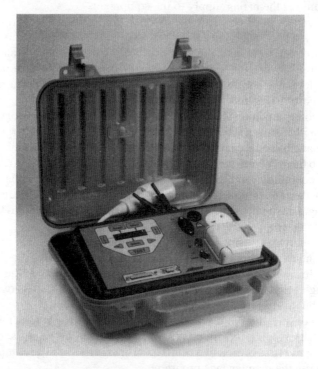

Figure 13.5 - Portable Appliance Tester (Courtesy of Metrotest Instruments)

windings as a safety precaution to stop the primary higher voltage appearing on the secondary winding. An insulation resistance check is therefore required to prove that the primary is isolated from the screen and from the secondary winding. The unit should be checked to ensure that the socket-outlets used on the secondary side are the correct type for the voltage being used. This is work for a Category II competent person.

BS EN 60309 (BS4343) Plugs and sockets colour code

Discrimination between different voltages is achieved by using coloured socket-outlets and plug tops and by positioning the earth contact in a different position relative to the keyway as shown in Figure 13.6.

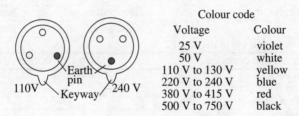

Colour code	
Voltage	Colour
25 V	violet
50 V	white
110 V to 130 V	yellow
220 V to 240 V	blue
380 V to 415 V	red
500 V to 750 V	black

Figure 13.6 - Colour code BS EN 60309 (BS4343) sockets

Small portable generators

Portable generators up to about 5 kW are considered to be small, nevertheless they still require attention. The manufacturer should be consulted to determine whether any part of the generator winding is referenced to the frame by an internal connection. The unit should be checked to ensure that the star point of a three-phase unit or one pole of a single-phase unit are connected to the earthing conductor for the electrical system. It should be noted that if RCDs are installed for additional protection, they will not work unless there is an earth back to the generator. As with transformers, check that the correct type of sockets have been installed for the voltage, that overload and short-circuit protection has been installed, that the earth connections are sound, that the unit is not damaged and that all mechanical guards are in place. Also obtain from the manufacturer a complete maintenance schedule and comply with it.

Records

There is no requirement in the regulations for records to be kept; the problem is, how do you prove that maintenance has been carried out if records are not kept? Additionally, maintenance records are recommended in HSE PM32 and in the Code of Practice on the Provision and Use of Work Equipment Regulations.

Without records, even in the simplest form, no person can remember when a piece of equipment was last inspected let alone tested. To keep a record each item of equipment requires identifying with a number which can be entered in the record book or in the computer if a maintenance programme is being used. This means each item, even short lengths of connecting lead and extension leads. Where a large quantity of different types of portable appliances are being used the numbering system can be alphanumeric.

As a guide Figure 13.7 gives a maintenance chart which can be modified to suit a particular maintenance programme.

Type of equipment		Date purchased		Equip. N°		
Make		Voltage		Rating		
Conditions in which normally used						
Items inspected and checked	Inspection results					
Equipment check						
No damage or deterioration						
Cable sheath in cord grip						
Cable will not pull out of cord grip						
Brushes (if any) checked						
Line, Neutral, Earth connections correct						
Connections tight						
Dust - Dirt - removed						
Insulation resistance L/N to earth						
Correct type for conditions of use						
Plug or cable coupler check						
No damage or deterioration						
Cable sheath in cord grip						
Cable will not pull out of cord grip						
Correct voltage rating						
Line, Neutral, Earth connections correct						
Connections tight						
Correct size of fuse fitted						
Cable check						
No damage at entry to plug						
No damage at entry to equipment						
No damage throughout length of cable						
Correct type for conditions of use						
Continuity of cores from plug to						
equipment Phase						
Neutral						
Earth						
Insulation resistance						
Plug to equipment - Phase / Neutral to Earth						
Additional checks on a transformer						
Secondary insulation resistance to earth						
Insulation resistance primary to secondary						
Additional checks on complete equipment						
after major repair Load test						
Flash Test						
Operation test						
Earth leakage test						
Label "Not to be used after label" fitted and dated						
Person checking equipment						
Name in block capitals						
Signature:						
Date:						

Figure 13.7 - Maintenance chart

Chapter 14

Cutting off the supply

Whenever electrical maintenance or an electrical inspection and test is carried out invariably the electrical supply has to be isolated. The electrical supply has also to be isolated to allow mechanical maintenance to be carried out.

Regulation 3 of the Management of Heath and Safety at Work Regulations (MHSW Regulations) requires an assessment to be made of the risks to the health and safety of the employees to which they are exposed whilst they are at work.

Such risks when carrying out maintenance on electrical equipment are concerned with; persons touching live parts, operating switchgear incorrectly causing it to explode, the risks associated with arcing and the risks associated with using test instruments. Additionally, the Provision and Use of Work Equipment Regulations (PUWER) require action concerning specific risks and hazards.

Regulation 7 (PUWER): Specific risks

(1) Where the use of work equipment is likely to involve a specific risk to health or safety, every employer shall ensure that -

(a) the use of that work equipment is restricted to those persons given the task of using it; and

(b) repairs, modifications, maintenance or servicing of that work equipment is restricted to those persons who have been specifically designated to perform operations of that description (whether or not also authorised to perform other operations).

(2) The employer shall ensure that the persons designated for the purposes of sub-paragraph (b) of paragraph (1) have received adequate training related to any operations in respect of which they have been so designated.

Specific hazards are also covered by the PUWE Regulations.

Regulation 12 : (PUWER) Protection against specified hazards

(1) Every employer shall take measures to ensure that the exposure of a person using work equipment to any risk to his health or safety from any hazard specified in paragraph (3) is either prevented, or, where that is not reasonably practicable, adequately controlled.

(3)(b) rupture or disintegration of parts of work equipment;

(3)(c) work equipment catching fire or overheating;

(3)(d) the unintended or premature discharge of any article or of any gas, dust, liquid, vapour or other substance which, in each case, is produced, used or stored in the work equipment;

(3)(e) the unintended or premature explosion of the work equipment or any article or substance produced, used or stored in it.

The Electricity at Work Regulations (EAWR) contain specific requirements concerned with the isolation of electrical equipment.

Regulation 12(1): *(EAWR) Subject to paragraph (3), where necessary to prevent danger, suitable means (including, where appropriate, methods of identifying circuits) shall be available for -*

(a) cutting off the supply of electrical energy to any electrical equipment; and

(b) the isolation of any electrical equipment.

EAW Regulation 12(1) requires that where it is necessary to prevent danger, suitable means of cutting off the supply of electrical energy to any electrical equipment and the isolation of electrical equipment, shall be provided. Where confusion could arise the regulation also calls for the circuits to be identified.

Regulation 12(1) has therefore two requirements, the first is for cutting off the supply to prevent danger, commonly known as emergency switching, and the second is for isolation of electrical equipment, which is required to allow work to be carried out on the equipment.

The regulation includes the words 'where necessary to prevent danger', which means an assessment of the likely danger in normal and abnormal conditions has to be made. This assessment is also covered by Regulation 3 of the MHSW Regulations mentioned at the beginning of this chapter. The assessment must take into account the environmental conditions as detailed in Regulation 6 of the EAW Regulations and which equipment could be a source of danger if such means was not provided, together with the installation and the operation and maintenance requirements over the life of the equipment.

Emergency switching

Switching off to prevent danger means providing emergency switching, which is defined in the IEE Wiring Regulations as:

An operation intended to remove, as quickly as possible, danger, which may have occurred unexpectedly.

Emergency switching has therefore to be provided at every point at which it may be necessary to disconnect the supply rapidly to prevent or remove a hazard. Hazards can be associated with machinery, such as a single machine, a continuous production line, or conveyors.

In this respect parts of Regulations 15 to 19 of the PUWE Regulations are relevant and are given at the end of this chapter.

The emergency switching device can be either the manual operation of a switch or the remote operation of a contactor by a stop button. Whichever device is used it must be capable of being restrained in the off position and must be suitable for any normal and abnormal operating conditions, such as the conditions imposed by a stalled motor, and must be capable of cutting off the supply with a single action. The emergency switch should only be associated with one item of electrical equipment, but can be common to several items of equipment where these are energised and de-energised as a group.

The emergency switching device should be suitably located in accordance with the type of risk present and should take into account the availability of the personnel available to operate them, identification of the emergency switching device with the equipment it controls is essential and the switch must be easily accessible.

Where contactors or circuit breakers are operated by remote emergency stop buttons, they must be arranged to operate on de-energisation of the coils. An isolator cannot be used as an emergency switch, since it is not designed to make or break load current.

The colour of the emergency switching device is not specified in the regulations but the accepted colour is red.

Emergency switching is intended for use by any person in order to prevent or remove a hazard; although not a requirement of the regulations, all personnel working in the vicinity should therefore be acquainted with its location and its purpose.

Isolation

Regulations 12(1)b and (2) of the EAW Regulations are both concerned with isolation. Where it is necessary to prevent danger Regulation 12(1)b calls for the isolation of any electrical equipment.

Such a danger exists when work has to be carried out on parts that are usually live in normal use. EAW Regulation 12(2) is worded to ensure that isolation is complete from every source of electrical energy.

Regulation 12(2): In paragraph (1), "isolation" means the disconnection and separation of the electrical equipment from every source of electrical energy in such a way that this disconnection and separation is secure.

Regulation 19 of the PUWE Regulations is also concerned with isolation and calls for suitable isolation to be provided and clearly identified.

In damp situations motors are quite often provided with heaters inside to limit condensation within the motor, the circuits are designed so that the heater is switched on when the motor is switched off. In these circumstances the isolator at the motor must isolate both the power supply to the motor and the supply to the heating unit in the winding of the motor. Another example of dual supplies going into equipment is with control circuits which derive their supply from a different source of power from that of the equipment. For isolation to be complete all sources must be isolated.

Principle and purpose

The principle of isolation is to ensure that normally live parts are made dead before work commences, the purpose of isolation is to ensure the supply cannot be restored by a remote switch or control circuit. Furthermore the electrical equipment to be worked on should not be accepted as safe until it has been proved dead by testing. Testing to prove that a circuit or piece of equipment is dead is considered to be live working, so the precautions called for by EAW Regulation 14 have to be used.

Regulation 14: No person shall be engaged in any work activity on or so near any live conductor (other than one suitably covered with insulating material so as to prevent danger) that danger may arise unless -

(a) it is unreasonable in all the circumstances for it to be dead; and

(b) it is reasonable in all the circumstances for him to be at work on or near it while it is live; and

(c) suitable precautions (including where necessary the provision of suitable protective equipment) are taken to prevent injury.

When checking that isolation is complete the test instrument should be proved before the test is made and proved again afterwards to ensure that the equipment is dead. This means that personnel who are going to be allowed to isolate equipment must have received training on how to do it properly and how to be aware of the dangers that could be present.

Isolation by non-electrical personnel

Isolation can also include the isolation of equipment that is permanently being taken out of service, and can be used to enable non-electrical work to be carried out. However, where non-electrical personnel use isolators to enable mechanical work to be carried out, they should be taught as part of their training that the load must be switched off first, since isolators are not designed to switch load on or off.

It is better to have the isolator interlocked with a load breaking device so that the load is switched off before the isolator's contacts open. This can be achieved by using isolators with additional contacts which break first and make last. These contacts are then wired into the stop circuit of the controlling contactor, which disconnects the load before the isolator contacts start to open. This arrangement also has the advantage that the equipment can only be restarted in the proper manner at the starter. This also stops the practice of the equipment being started and stopped by the isolator; a function it was not designed to do.

Basic rules for isolation

Where an isolating device for a particular circuit or electrical equipment is to be placed in a remote position from the equipment to be isolated, then a means must be provided for ensuring that the isolator cannot be inadvertently re-closed by another person, and that it cannot re-close through mechanical shock or vibration. Any lock or key provided for this purpose must not be interchangeable with any other within the same installation.

Where a single device is not capable of isolating all the live parts in an enclosure, a warning notice must be placed in such a position that a person gaining access to the enclosure is warned to isolate the other live parts elsewhere. Alternatively, a Castell key interlocking arrangement can be used so that access to the enclosure cannot be made until all circuits are isolated.

Where capacitors are used, such as for power factor correction at motors, then adequate means must be provided to discharge those capacitors before access to them is made.

It is preferable for isolation to be carried out using multipole devices, but single pole devices can be used providing they are adjacent to each other.

It is a requirement of EAW Regulation 12 and PUWE Regulation 19(2) that where it is not clear to the user what the isolator controls, then appropriate identification on the equipment should be provided. Such identification should take into account the environmental conditions, so that it does not rapidly become obliterated or disintegrate. This requirement also applies to distribution boards, which are often used to permanently isolate a circuit by the disconnection of the conductors. Without identification of which circuit each protective device controls, confusion must exist.

The location of isolators is important and must take into account the human factor, especially when they are used to enable adjustments to be made to equipment. A person who has to walk 300 metres to isolate and then switch on again after an adjustment is made, will soon decide not to bother if several adjustments have to be made before the correct one is found, thus defeating the whole idea of safety.

How devices comply as isolators

Not all devices can be used as isolators, those that can, have to comply with certain requirements:

1. They must have sufficient poles to disconnect all live conductors, (solid links are acceptable in neutrals where the circuit protective conductor is separately connected to the main earth bar, i.e. TN system).
2. They must have a sufficient air gap or effective dielectric between opened contacts.
3. They must have adequate creepage and clearance distances.
4. They must not be able to close through mechanical shock or vibration.
5. They must be provided with a means of stopping unauthorised, improper, or unintentional energisation.

6. The position of the contacts should be either:-

    (a)   externally visible;

    (b)   clearly and reliably indicated; or

    (c)   give an indication of the isolated position only when the specified isolating distance has been achieved on each pole.

In certain circumstances, both the phase and neutral conductor will require isolation such as: where the electrical equipment has heated surfaces that can be touched, or with electrode water heaters, boilers, and immersion heaters.

An isolator is a mechanical switching device, so semiconductor devices, limit switches, touch switches etc., cannot be used as isolators.

Where it is intended to use miniature circuit breakers (MCBs) or moulded case circuit breakers (MCCBs) as isolators, it should first be ascertained from the manufacturer of the device, that it is suitable for use as an isolator, since its primary function is that of a circuit breaker.

What can be used as isolators

An isolator is referred to as a disconnector in British Standards and would comply with the above requirements, but it is only suitable for off load disconnection, since it is not designed to make or break load current.

An isolating switch, referred to as a switch disconnector in British Standards, can be used providing it is a mechanical switching device and complies with the above requirements. Switches are designed to make and break load current.

Plugs and sockets can be used for isolation; however, where the load exceeds 16 amps they should be switched socket outlets, the switch preferably being interlocked with the plug top.

Fuse links are only really suitable for off load disconnection, consideration has to be given to what would happen if the fuse was replaced onto a fault, and how stopping someone else replacing a fuse in the wrong fuseway is to be prevented. A distribution board that is lockable is no safeguard against danger, since they all tend to have the same type and number of key; which makes the interior accessible to anyone. Replacing the withdrawn fuses with empty carriers suitably labelled, is one way of preventing someone else replacing a fuse in the wrong fuseway, but is a poor substitute for proper isolation and requires a code of safe working practice to be set up and Category II competent persons to use it.

Who is allowed to isolate ?

There are no requirements in the EAW Regulations for the appointment of Authorised Persons or that workers must be accompanied, nor is there any age limit specified. This does not mean that anyone is allowed to isolate or work on equipment.

Who is allowed to isolate is determined by EAW Regulation 16:

Regulation 16: No person shall be engaged in any work activity where technical knowledge or experience is necessary to prevent danger or, where appropriate, injury, unless he possesses such knowledge or experience, or is under such degree of supervision as may be appropriate having regard to the nature of the work.

Since a circuit or piece of electrical equipment cannot be considered dead until a fail-safe test is made, danger must be considered to be present. The person who is isolating the equipment must have received such training or be under such a degree of supervision that injury will not occur.

This is very appropriate in the advent of multi-skilling in industry, the person isolating must have received training in the procedure to be adopted in isolation and must have been made aware of the dangers electricity may create. As already mentioned training is also a requirement of the HSW Act, the Management of Health and Safety at Work Regulations and the Provision and Use of Work Equipment Regulations.

Safety can only be assured for a person; if that person is sure the isolator is off, is sure it cannot accidentally re-close, is sure no other person can restore the supply and that a fail-safe test has been carried out to ensure the equipment really is dead.

The effect of Regulation 16, and the other regulations mentioned above, is that your staff will require grading into what they are capable of, or have been trained to do. Supervisors must have a greater knowledge of the work function than the men working under them, if accidents are to be avoided.

EAW Regulation 12(3)

Regulation 12(3): Paragraph (1) shall not apply to electrical equipment which is itself a source of electrical energy but, in such a case as is necessary, precautions shall be taken to prevent, so far as is reasonably practicable, danger.

Regulation 12(3) recognises that it is impracticable in certain circumstances to switch off or isolate, for instance it is not possible to switch off batteries, the windings of generators, exciters, or capacitors; capacitors should of course have a discharging resistor installed in them. Even so, this regulation still requires precautions to be taken to prevent danger, this would take the form of identifying the hazards, warning personnel of the hazards, giving clear instructions how such installations should be undertaken and maintained, and using staff who have been trained or who are experienced in that kind of work.

Warning employees of possible hazards is also a requirement of Regulation 7 of the Management of Health and Safety at Work Regulations (MHSWR).

EAW Regulation 13

The requirements of Regulation 13 have already been partially covered, but EAW Regulation 13 refers to adequate precautions being taken to prevent electrical equipment that has been isolated, from becoming electrically charged.

Regulation 13: *Adequate precautions shall be taken to prevent electrical equipment, which has been made dead in order to prevent danger while work is carried out on or near that equipment, from becoming electrically charged during that work if danger may thereby arise.*

It specifies electrical equipment which by definition includes any cables, conductors, wires etc.

From becoming electrically charged, means that it is either made live from its own power sources or has become charged with electrical energy through induction or capacitance.

EAW Regulation 13 is calling for proper working procedures to be adopted such as, having a code of safe working practice, ensuring that when isolation has been made the equipment to be worked on is proved dead by testing and that the isolators have been padlocked off. Any instrument used for checking the equipment or cables are dead should be proved before and after the test has been made and before any attempt is made to work on the equipment.

Where a group of people are to work on the equipment there should be a work schedule, so that each person knows what he or she has to do and they should not attempt to carry out any work until they are clear what is required. Where a group of people are concerned it is important that only one person is in overall charge of the work to be done and that person should ensure that each person in the group understands what they have to do. Other requirements of the regulation are ensuring that any exposed live equipment is completely shrouded, that warning notices are posted on the isolators or switches which have been used to switch off the power, that unique padlocks have been placed on such equipment (See figure 9.1 Chapter 9) so that no one else can restore the supply, and that danger notices are placed on any adjacent live equipment.

If the proper isolation procedures are carried out on a low voltage system, the danger of the equipment becoming live from normal sources is removed. It can, however, become charged by induction, or from capacitors connected to the system which have been overlooked. Becoming charged by induction is particularly true with high voltage electrical equipment, where there is latent energy stored in the system, particularly with high voltage cables.

On high voltage networks, the system should be isolated and then earthed at the switchgear, but secondary earths (temporary earths) will be required at the point work is being carried out, since the cables to the equipment can become charged due to them being local to other live cables. Another important point to take into consideration, is that high voltage cables remain charged for a considerable time after they have been isolated, due to capacitance in the cable.

Where work is to be carried out on a high voltage system, a permit-to-work system is required. If additional work is discovered to be needed whilst working on the equipment, no attempt should be made to do this work, until a further permit-to-work has been obtained covering the additional work.

Isolation is to enable work to be carried out on equipment that is normally live and so EAW Regulation 15 must be taken into account and adequate working space, adequate access and adequate lighting must be provided. Adequate, means that when switchgear is racked out of its housing, there is still sufficient space to work on the equipment and that it does not stop exit from the room or building by anyone, should an emergency arise.

Any test instruments provided to ensure equipment is dead before work commences have to be suitable for the use intended and be maintained and properly used to comply with EAW Regulation 4(4).

Regulation 4(4): Any equipment provided under these Regulations for the purpose of protecting persons at work on or near electrical equipment shall be suitable for the use for which it is provided, be maintained in a condition suitable for that use, and be properly used.

Account should also be taken of Regulation 8 of the Provision and Use of Work Equipment Regulations (PUWER).

Provision and Use of Work Equipment Regulations

*Regulation 8 (PUWER): **Information and instructions***
  (1) *Every employer shall ensure that all persons who use work equipment have available to them adequate health and safety information and, where appropriate, written instructions pertaining to the use of the work equipment.*
  (2) *Every employer shall ensure that any of his employees who supervises or manages the use of work equipment has available to him adequate health and safety information and, where appropriate, written instructions pertaining to the use of the work equipment. .... etc.*

*Regulation 15 (PUWER): **Stop controls***
  (1) *Every employer shall ensure that, where appropriate, work equipment is provided with one or more readily accessible controls the operation of which will bring the work equipment to a safe condition in a safe manner.*
  (2) *Any control required by paragraph (1) shall bring the work equipment to a complete stop where necessary for reasons of health and safety.*
  (3) *Any control required by paragraph (1) shall, if necessary for reasons of health and safety, switch off all sources of energy after stopping the functioning of the work equipment.*

(4)   *Any control required by paragraph (1) shall operate in priority to any control which starts or changes the operating conditions of the work equipment.*

Regulation 16 *(PUWER): Emergency stop controls*
(1)   *Every employer shall ensure that, where appropriate, work equipment is provided with one or more readily accessible emergency stop controls unless it is not necessary by reason of the nature of the hazards and the time is taken for the work equipment to come to a complete stop as a result of the action of any control provided by virtue of regulation 15(1).*
(2)   *Any control required by paragraph (1) shall operate in priority to any control required by regulation 15(1).*

Regulation 17 *(PUWER): Controls*
(1)   *Every employer shall ensure that all controls for work equipment shall be clearly visible and identifiable, including by appropriate marking where necessary.*
(2)   *Except where necessary, the employer shall ensure that no control for work equipment is in a position where any person operating the control is exposed to a risk to his health or safety.*
(3)   *..................... etc.*

Regulation 18 *(PUWER): Control systems*
(1)   *Every employer shall ensure, so far as is reasonably practicable, that all control systems of work equipment are safe.*
(2)   *Without prejudice to the generality of paragraph (1), a control system shall not be safe unless -*
(a)   *its operation does not create any increased risk to health or safety;*
(b)   *it ensures, so far as is reasonably practicable, that any fault in or damage to any part of the control system or the loss of supply of any source of energy used by the work equipment cannot result in additional or increased risk to health or safety;*
(c)   *it does not impede the operation of any control required by   PUWER Regulations 15 or 16.*

Regulation 19 *(PUWER): Isolation from sources of energy*
(1)   *Every employer shall ensure that where appropriate work equipment is provided with suitable means to isolate it from all its sources of energy.*
(2)   *Without prejudice to the generality of paragraph (1), the means mentioned in that paragraph shall not be suitable unless they are clearly identifiable and readily accessible.*
(3)   *Every employer shall take appropriate measures to ensure that reconnection of any energy source to work equipment does not expose any person using the work equipment to any risk to his health or safety.*

Chapter 15

Work Activity - operation and use of system

Personnel affected by the regulations

The EAW Regulation 4(3) is the regulation that brings all personnel, whether they be managers, engineers, architects, office workers, plumbers, decorators or bricklayers within the scope of the regulations.

Regulation 4(3): *Every work activity, including operation, use and maintenance of a system and work near a system, shall be carried out in such a manner as not to give rise, so far as is reasonably practicable, to danger.*

Work activity would include the painting or decorating of premises where a danger could exist from the system, such as inside a high voltage or low voltage substation, particularly if it contained open type switchgear.

The danger is not confined to substations, carrying out any work activity near the electrical system where danger is present needs careful consideration. Carrying out work near the electrical down shop leads for an overhead crane is one area where danger is present and requires a safe system of working to be applied, with the addition of a permit to work system, so that safety can be ensured.

Plumbers and fitters can be in danger when they least expect it. The bonding of the mechanical services to the main electrical earth bar has been covered in a previous chapter, where it was also explained that a fault within the building will cause a voltage to appear between exposed and extraneous conductive parts. However, when there is an electrical fault electricity will take the route of least resistance, an earth fault can therefore cause some current to flow down the mechanical services pipes back to the main earth bar. A fitter cutting such a pipe then becomes in series with the current. The current may not be sufficient to kill the fitter, but the unexpected electrical shock could be sufficient to make him fall off a ladder and be injured. The rule here is that an electrical bond should always be put across pipes which are going to be altered. On small pipes a battery jump-lead as used with the car battery should be sufficient. The problem is that the fitter does not know whether the pipe is, or is not, carrying leakage current. Using a bond across the pipe would be 'the other suitable means' referred to in EAW Regulation 8.

Regulation 8 : *Precautions shall be taken, either by earthing or by <u>other suitable means</u>, to prevent danger arising when any conductor (other than a circuit conductor) which may reasonably foreseeably become charged as a result of either the use of a system, or a fault in a system, becomes so charged; -------- etc.*

The self employed painter and decorator is also covered by this part of the EAW Regulations. In the simplest form he wets the walls to enable him to scrape off the old paper, but the walls contain socket outlets and lighting switches. The decorator invariably loosens these electrical items to enable him to remove the paper from behind them and then later to enable him to tuck the new paper behind them. In both cases he is putting water near electrical items. He may, of course, use a steamer to remove the paper, in this case he is using electrical equipment and is covered by the EAW Regulations. Similarly the bricklayer is covered by the EAW Regulations when he mixes the cement in an electrically driven cement mixer.

EAW Regulation 4(3) along with EAW Regulation 8, also covers work on construction sites, which have the hidden dangers of underground cables and overhead lines. As far as underground cables are concerned one of the safety measures to be taken is to use a cable locator before any work commences. Where overhead lines are concerned it is a requirement of EAW Regulation 8 that any conductor must not become charged. Precautions to be taken would include barriers to stop personnel and equipment approaching too near the overhead lines, with warning notices making staff and plant drivers aware of the dangers. Where plant has to cross under the line the usual goal post arrangement is used to ensure a minimum distance between plant and the line, however, if steel catenary wires are used to indicate the maximum height, then these must be earthed to discharge any induced voltage as shown in Figure 15.1.

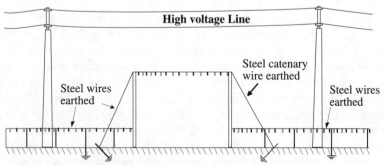

Figure 15.1 - Earthing catenary wires near overhead lines

These precautions are not confined to construction sites, many factories have bare overhead lines passing between buildings.

Before any work is carried out round the factory complex or on a construction site, a check has to be made to ascertain that there are no underground cables. This entails checking site plans, and using cable locators, such cable locators will however, be subject to EAW Regulation 4(4).

Regulation 4(4): Any equipment provided under these Regulations for the purpose of protecting persons at work on or near electrical equipment shall be suitable for the use for which it is provided, be maintained in a condition suitable for that use, and be properly used.

Equipment provided for protecting persons at work

Equipment provided for the protection of persons comprises:

Cable locators.

High voltage test equipment

Low voltage test equipment

Rubber gloves, rubber mats, insulating screens, insulated tools etc.

110 V transformers for use with portable equipment etc.

Residual current devices

EAW Regulation 4(4) is not qualified by 'so far as is reasonably practicable' nor does it refer to injury or the risk of injury. The impact of this regulation is that where protective equipment is provided it must be in a condition suitable for the use for which it is required, it must be maintained in that condition and properly used.

This means that the equipment must be regularly tested and maintained. The proper use of the equipment entails personnel being properly trained how to use the equipment, as in the case of using cable locators.

Where rubber gloves are used for electrical purposes they should be manufactured to BS 697, which specifies that they should be stored unfolded at a temperature between 10 °C and 21 °C, they should also be issued in a container free from grease and oil and should be examined inside and outside before they are used.

Gloves that are frequently used should be re-tested at intervals of not more than six months and in any event not more than twelve months, even if they have never been used. The test that the gloves should be subjected to and how they should be tested, is given in BS 697. This British Standard is the standard accepted, since it is an Approved Code of Practice, the implications of which were discussed earlier. The effect of BS 697 is that a contravention of the Approved Code occurs when gloves are left lying around on benches, are not stored correctly and not regularly tested.

Depending upon the number of gloves in use and the amount they are used may mean that the most economic way of complying with the Approved Code is to change them for new ones every six months, even so, they must still be handled properly and the other requirements of BS 697 must be observed.

To comply with safety requirements, test instruments used on the low voltage network will require fusible leads (Figure 15.2) to protect the user if he accidentally switches the meter to a current range when measuring the voltage between phases. The overload protection fuse in the instrument is of no use whatsoever for protecting personnel. The HSE will frown on any company or person using such test instruments without fusible leads since the risks are high. The high rupturing capacity fuse in the leads is there to cut off the short-circuit current rapidly, limiting the energy let through in the event of the instrument being used on the wrong range.

All test equipment should be regularly checked to ensure there is no possibility of a null indication giving rise to danger.

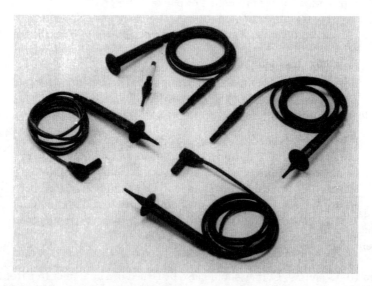

Figure 15.2 - Two types of fusible leads - (Courtesy of Metrotest Instruments.)

Operation

Operation of electrical equipment should only be made by those who have been trained how to operate the equipment and are aware of the dangers that can arise. For instance, accidents have happened in the past with high voltage isolators which are designed to carry a short-circuit current only for the length of time the main circuit breaker takes to operate, they are not designed to break such a current.

Accidents have happened where an isolator has been earthed on a ring main, and the operator at another isolator has switched power on to the earthed cable. Realising the mistake he has then immediately tried to switch it off. This has caused explosions in the switch tanks, resulting in fire, causing serious injury and death to the operator. More modern isolators are fitted with an arrangement whereby the operator has to remove the handle and reverse it, before the drive mechanism can be moved again. The object is to delay the reverse operating of the isolator for about 3 seconds, thus giving the main supply breaker time to trip, in the event of a wrong switch action.

Accidents have also occurred with the older type of oil circuit breaker where they have been operated onto a fault. The problem with the older type of circuit breaker is the speed of closing or opening the breaker is dependant upon the operator. If the breaker is not closed in a decisive way and is closed onto a fault, an explosion can occur causing serious injuries to the operator.

The modern approach is for the remote operation of the breakers, but this still requires the operators to be trained for the duties they have to perform.

There is no mention in the regulations of permits-to-work or for the appointment of Authorised Persons, but these will clearly be required where high voltage equipment is operated and maintained.

Operation also includes starting motors, and proper procedures are required where the unexpected starting of a motor can give rise to danger at other parts of the plant.

Maintenance personnel

EAW Regulation 4(3) is also concerned with maintenance but in this case how it is carried out.

Regulation 4 (3): Every work activity, including operation, use and maintenance of a system and work near a system, shall be carried out in such a manner as not to give rise, so far as is reasonably practicable, to danger.

Maintenance must be carried out by a competent person who has received training in the type of maintenance that has to be carried out. This is important since it is a requirement of EAW Regulation 16 that no person shall be engaged in any work activity where technical knowledge or experience is necessary to prevent danger. For example, only personnel experienced, or who have been trained to carry out maintenance on high voltage switchgear, or in the maintenance of batteries, should be allowed to carry out maintenance on such items, because of the hidden dangers. EAW Regulation 16 is concerned with persons being competent. It includes being competent to maintain equipment including portable electrical equipment. Competency with one type of equipment or system does not necessarily mean being competent with different equipment or systems.

Regulation 16: No person shall be engaged in any work activity where technical knowledge or experience is necessary to prevent danger or, where appropriate injury, unless he possesses such knowledge or experience, or is under such degree of supervision as may be appropriate have regard to the nature of the work.

A chartered civil engineer may be competent, but he is not electrically competent, unless he has received training.

It means that the employer, manager, engineer, foreman, or chargehand has to be certain that the person selected: can do - knows how to do - the work he has been asked to do.

Regulation 4(3) covers every work activity and is therefore not confined to electrical staff, since it includes work carried out near a system. Non-electrical maintenance staff fall into this category, so a code of safe working practice is essential, not only for the electrical staff, but for other staff who carry out work on equipment driven or controlled by electrical means.

Where the work activity is maintenance of electrical equipment, it is important to make certain that the person who is to carry out the work is competent (i.e. is fully experienced or has been trained) to do so and that a safe procedure of working has been worked out.

Use of the system

The use of the system involves almost everyone; the modern office is full of electrical equipment which is used by non-electrical personnel. The company, manager, or supervisor will have to ensure that using the equipment does not give rise to danger and that staff are instructed not to interfere with equipment.

There was a case, not long ago, where an industrial chemist was killed in a laboratory. He had apparently removed the cover off some equipment containing a cathode-ray tube (TV screen) which was at a very high voltage; he was working on his own at the time, so no one knows the reason for the cover being removed from the equipment. When he was found, the current path was obvious, since the hand print was on the screen and the floor was black where he was kneeling.

These are the kind of accidents that have to be guarded against. Staff can be instructed not to interfere with equipment, but it is difficult to stop them when they are unaccompanied.

Accidents occurring when electricity is being used, resulting in injury from electric shock, electric burn, electric explosion or arcing, or from fire or explosion initiated by electrical energy, are covered by the Electricity at Work Regulations, but accidents caused by the failure of an electrical device, such as a limit switch, are covered by the Health and Safety at Work etc. Act.

Live working

EAW Regulation 4(3) is not the only regulation concerned with non-electrical activities, EAW Regulation 14 is also involved since it covers all persons.

Regulation 14: *No person shall be engaged in any work activity on or so near any live conductor (other than one suitably covered with insulating material so as to prevent danger) that danger may arise unless -*
   (a) it is unreasonable in all the circumstances for it to be dead; and

(b) it is reasonable in all the circumstances for him to be at work on or near it while it is live; and

(c) suitable precautions (including where necessary the provision of suitable protective equipment) are taken to prevent injury.

EAW Regulation 14 is of course only applicable where persons are at work on or near live electrical equipment which may foreseeably give rise to danger. This includes work carried out near underground cables and overhead lines, working near the bare crane down shop leads mentioned previously or working near live socket-outlets and switches.

Accidents to maintenance staff can occur with simple operations being carried out. An electrician was killed fitting an MCB into a distribution board while it was still live. Another electrician was killed drilling a hole in a distribution board for a conduit. Again the distribution board had not been made dead and as the hole was completed the cutter and drill went into the distribution board and touched one of the phase bars. In another instance an electrician was working on equipment that was dead. He was removing a disused conduit from the gable end of the building. To do this he was working off the overhead crane and as he removed the conduit it touched the live downshop leads for the crane. He was killed.

Where such work is carried out the duty holder, that is the person instructing the work to be done, has to comply with (a), (b) and (c) of Regulation 14. This means that he must be able to prove that it was unreasonable for the conductors to be dead, that it was reasonable for the work to be carried out whilst the conductor was live and that suitable protective equipment had been provided in accordance with EAW Regulation 4(4), to ensure that there would be no injury to the persons carrying out the work. He will also have to prove that the person carrying out the work had been suitably trained and was competent in accordance with EAW Regulation 16.

Danger is always present when work is carried out on or near live conductors, if only from electric shock. What Regulation 14 is saying is that the equipment or conductors should be made dead before any work is carried out.

EAW Regulation 14 is there to dissuade live working since most of the accidents occurring could have been avoided if the power had been switched off. Where accidents occur in the future whilst a person is working live, prosecution by the HSE will probably be inevitable.

Regulation 14 does recognise that there are situations where it would be unreasonable for the work to be made dead. For instance, it would be unreasonable for a local electricity company to switch off the supply to an industrial estate whilst they made a cable joint, or it may be impossible on a construction site to have overhead lines or underground cables made dead. Similarly, a production line with variable speed drives controlled by electronic equipment, may require potentiometers to be adjusted, which cannot be done with the power off.

EAW Regulation 14 in such circumstances requires precautions to be taken so that no injury will occur. Such precautions would involve the use of insulating screens and training personnel in the dangers of working with live equipment. Other precautions include the use of transparent plastic screens covering equipment, with holes in the screen to allow the test prod of an instrument through to the live terminal. Any such hole must not exceed IP2X.

Live working includes testing to find a fault. If this is not possible with the equipment dead then the same stringent safety precautions are required. It must be remembered that testing a circuit that has become dead, to find out where there is a fault, is the same as working live, since the circuit will be live at the point of fault. The greater the risk the less reason there is for live working. The risk of burns may be minimal, but the risk of injury from electric shock is always present.

Working unaccompanied

The regulations do not require a person to be accompanied. An assessment has therefore to be made as to whether a second person will make the conditions safer.

Accidents happen when persons working on live conductors get distracted. A second person could probably make the work safer by keeping other people away from the area where live conductors are being worked on, thus reducing the possibility of distraction.

Consideration has also to be given to the degree of danger and whether a second person should be present in case the person working on the equipment gets into difficulties. The second person does not have to be skilled in the work being carried out, but must have knowledge of the dangers that are present and must know what to do in the case of an emergency. This means that he should have been trained especially in what to do if a person is receiving an electric shock and how to carry out resuscitation. The St. John Ambulance Association will run courses for companies on artificial respiration.

Selection of equipment

When selecting equipment to be used it is important to take into consideration the environmental conditions that are or could be applicable.

Regulation 5 (PUWER) : Suitability of work equipment
- *(1) Every employer shall ensure that work equipment is so constructed or adapted as to be suitable for the purpose for which it is used or provided.*
- *(2) In selecting work equipment, every employer shall have regard to the working conditions and to the risks to the health and safety of persons which exist in the premises or undertaking in which that work equipment is to be used and any additional risk posed by the use of that work equipment.*

(3) Every employer shall ensure that work equipment is used only for operations for which, and under conditions for which, it is suitable.

(4) In this regulation "suitable" means suitable in any respect which it is reasonably foreseeable will affect the health or safety of any person.

This regulation means that equipment that is not designed for use in wet areas or hazardous areas, must not be used in those areas. It also means that the equipment should be used in accordance with the manufacturer's instructions.

It also means that other risks have to be taken into account. For instance, if a person is to work in a wet well or in a steel container where the resistance to earth in those areas is practically zero, consideration should be given to using either battery operated electrical equipment or compressed air. It must not be forgotten that the biggest danger from double insulated tools is the cable lead; whilst the lead has insulated cores contained in an insulating outer sheath it is very easily damaged. PUWE Regulation 5(2) therefore requires an assessment to be made of the area where the equipment is to be used and any risks that may arise.

PUWE Regulation 5(3) is self explanatory, but PUWE Regulation 5(4) means that consideration has to be given to the conditions that might occur. It could be a bright summer's day, but it could rain before the work is completed.

Electric shock first aid notice

Except for mines, the Electricity at Work Regulations do not require an electric shock first aid notice to be displayed. It would be a sensible precaution to display notices giving details of first aid for electric shock in all locations where such a danger is present. In any event, such notices ought to be displayed in substations, switchrooms and near control panels.

Chapter 16

Duty holders

One of the most important aspects of the Electricity at Work Regulations is that of duty holder, as spelt out in Regulation 3.

Regulation 3 : *(1) Except where otherwise expressly provided in these Regulations, it shall be the duty of every -*

(a)   employer and self employed person to comply with the provisions of these Regulations in so far as they relate to matters which are within his control; and

(b)   manager of a mine or quarry (within in either case the meaning of section 180 of the Mines and Quarries Act 1954 (a)) to ensure that all requirements or prohibitions imposed by or under these Regulations are complied with is so far as they relate to the mine or quarry or part of a quarry of which he is the manager and to matters which are within his control.

(2)   It shall be the duty of every employee while at work -

(a)   to cooperate with his employer so far as is necessary to enable any duty placed on that employer by the provisions of these Regulations to be complied with; and

(b)   to comply with the provisions of these regulations in so far as they relate to matters which are within his control.

Part III of the Electricity at Work Regulations, which has not been covered in this book, is devoted solely to mines. Regulation 3(1)(b) has been included above because the rest of the regulations, which are covered in this book, are also applicable to mines and quarries.

The self employed, as well as an employer, have to comply with the regulations where the system is under their control. The employee has two duties; the first one is to cooperate with the employer in applying work practices laid down by the employer, so as to comply with the regulations, and secondly to comply with the regulations himself.

The object of the regulation, is to ensure that all those who work with electricity are covered by the regulations. An employer is any person who employs one or more people under a contract of employment, or training under schemes to which the Health and Safety at Work etc. Act applies. A self employed person is an individual who may or may not employ other persons and who works for gain or reward even if he does not make a profit.

Extent of employer's responsibilities

Confusion may arise as to what extent the employer is responsible for the whole system, especially where they do not own the premises they occupy. Where the premises are freehold i.e. the employer owns the premises, he is responsible for the whole electrical system from the point of supply by the electricity supplier. Where the premises are small and the supply is delivered at low voltage, the point the responsibility starts is at the cable tails into the premises main isolator. The incoming cable, electricity supplier's fuses and meters, will be the responsibility of the electricity supplier, since the occupier is not allowed to touch this equipment.

Where the supply is delivered at high voltage, the point that responsibility changes from the electricity supplier to the consumer is less clear. It depends upon the arrangements made with the electricity supplier, for instance in medium sized factories the consumer provides the main substation, pays for the high voltage equipment and transformers which are installed by the electricity supplier. One or more employees of the occupier are then approved by the electricity supplier for entering the substation to carry out switching.

This is the grey area as to where the responsibilities of the electricity supplier cease and those of the occupier commence. Usually the electricity supplier is only responsible up to the high voltage metering. If the occupier's employees have not been trained and approved by the electricity supplier to maintain the high voltage switchgear, then a contract should be arranged with the electricity supplier to maintain the high voltage equipment and take responsibility under the regulations for the equipment, at the same time, clarifying with the electricity supplier where their responsibilities cease and those of the occupier commence.

In larger installations the same point of change over of responsibility should be determined. The occupier will then be responsible for the whole system from this point on, including all portable equipment that may be used with the system.

Where the premises are leasehold it will depend upon the terms of the lease. If the lease is a full repairing and maintaining lease, then the occupier will be responsible for the electrical system as though he owned the property.

Where the lessee just rents the accommodation and the electrical services are under the control of the landlord, i.e. the occupier is not allowed to alter the services, the responsibility of the occupier is for the equipment that is connected to the system. Although the landlord has no work activity with the electrical system, he is responsible under the HSW Act Section 4 for the electrical services throughout the premises and therefore responsible for the system under the Electricity at Work Regulations.

Where premises are occupied by several companies or firms and they share common entrances, passages and landings, the passages are under the control of the landlord who is the duty holder for those areas.

Individual's responsibility

As far as individuals are concerned, it will depend upon how much control they have over the work activity. The managing director of a company may not be carrying out electrical work, but he is in control of the company. His duty is to ensure that the person responsible for arranging for the work or maintenance to be carried out is competent to undertake such work and is doing his or her job properly.

Where that person does not carry out the work directly, their responsibility will be to lay down systems and methods of working that will be safe, and to organise the correct testing, inspection and maintenance of electrical equipment and ensure that it is carried out in a safe manner. It is also a requirement that he ensures that information is made available to the staff under his control.

Regulation 8 (PUWER): Information and instructions

(1) *Every employer shall ensure that all persons who use work equipment have available to them adequate health and safety information and, where appropriate, written instructions pertaining to the use of the work equipment.*

(2) *Every employer shall ensure that any of his employees who supervises or manages the use of work equipment has available to him adequate health and safety information and, where appropriate, written instructions pertaining to the use of the work equipment.*

(3) *Without prejudice to the generality of paragraphs (1) or (2), the information and instructions required by either of those paragraphs shall include information and, where appropriate, written instructions on -*

(a) *the conditions in which and the methods by which the work equipment may be used;*

(b) *foreseeable abnormal situations and the action to be taken if such a situation were to occur; and*

(c) *any conclusions to be drawn from experience in using the work equipment.*

(4) *Information and instructions required by this regulation shall be readily comprehensible to those concerned.*

Supervisors have a similar duty, but in addition, they must make certain that management rules are being obeyed, that the worker is complying with the regulations and that it is safe for work to be carried out. They have a further duty to ensure that the worker selected for a particular task is competent to carry out the type of work he has been asked to do, as required by EAW Regulation 16.

The person carrying out the work will have a duty to comply with any management rules for carrying out the work and to comply with the regulations by ensuring that his work activities are safe both to himself and other personnel. He should draw to the management's attention any work activity he feels is not complying with the law.

Part of Regulation 14** (MHSWR) : **Employees' duties

(2) *Every employee shall inform his employer or any other employee of that employer with specific responsibility for the health and safety of his fellow employees -*

(a) *of any work situation which a person with the first-mentioned employee's training and instruction would reasonably consider represented a serious and immediate danger to health and safety; and*

(b) *of any matter which a person with the first-mentioned employee's training and instruction would reasonably consider represented a shortcoming in the employer's protection arrangements for health and safety, ...etc.*

The size of a company varies from a one man company, to a company employing thousands of employees. The duties imposed on individuals will therefore vary, depending upon the size of the company. The responsibilities will depend upon the individuals control over the work activity; he does not necessarily have to be involved with electrical work to have duties under the regulations.

The directors of a company will be responsible for complying with and implementing the regulations. In most companies the directors will delegate these duties, but this does not delegate their responsibilities. They must make certain that where the work is delegated, it is properly carried out.

The directors will also have additional responsibilities, since they will have staff working directly under their control such as, secretaries, accountants, clerks etc. They will be responsible for ensuring that staff working near the electrical system are working without danger. They must ensure that equipment is not used where leads, plug tops etc., have become damaged. Additionally, they will be responsible for stopping any of their personal staff repairing plug tops with nail files etc. Even if the maintenance of the system has been delegated to a third party, it will be their responsibility to report to such staff any faults that have developed since it was last maintained.

Code of safe working practice

The only way it can be proved that the company's employees have received instructions is to have a written code of safe working practice because verbal communications can always be denied, especially in the event of an accident.

The code can be divided into parts; one for the office staff who use electrical equipment in the course of their work but who are not allowed to interfere with the electrical system, one part for non-electrical staff who use electrical equipment or who carry out non-electrical work near a system, and a part for the electrical staff detailing the safe procedures to adopt when maintaining or working with or near the electrical system.

Civil and mechanical engineers

Non-electrical personnel, such as civil and mechanical staff, have a duty under the regulations. Their duties can be detailed in a list.

- Personnel under their control are aware of and adhere to, the code of safe working practice when working with or near live electrical equipment.

- That any portable electric tools or generators used by personnel under their control are used in accordance with a safe code of working practice and are regularly tested and maintained by the electrical department.

- To ensure that any electrical equipment used is suitable for the adverse or hazardous situations in which it is to be used.

- That personnel are competent to use any electrical equipment they are supplied with and have been trained for the duties they have to perform.

- That work near live electrical equipment is supervised and personnel are made aware of any dangers.

- That any electrical equipment provided for protection against electrical accident is of the correct type, properly maintained and properly used.

- That inspections of equipment required are carried out and recorded.

Portable electric tools are always a source of danger. The cables to such equipment can so easily become damaged by being run over, being dragged over sharp surfaces, making contact with moving parts of machinery, being continually flexed close to the point of termination of the cable, or cables can be pulled out of a termination due to a loose or ineffective cord grip thereby disconnecting the earth wire; giving rise to a dangerous situation. Clearly, inspecting such items every month is inadequate. An inspection of the cable and terminations is essential before such equipment is used.

Other dangers that non-electrical workers should take into account is the cutting of non-electrical pipe work, since this can lead to electric shock. Precautions are required when digging or excavating, since there can be buried electric cables in the vicinity. Working near high voltage overhead lines can cause metalwork to become charged. Bare low voltage overhead lines between buildings can cause machinery to become live if touched, for instance by fork lift trucks. Painting near an overhead crane requires the electrical live down shop leads to be made dead. Where cable locators are used they must comply with EAW Regulation 4 (4) and staff must be trained how to use such protective devices.

Managers (non-electrical)

Managers, unless they have been trained, are not competent to deal with electrical equipment or installations. Their duties are to ensure that staff adhere to the code of safe working practice and report any equipment or cables that appear to have become damaged. The relatively simple operation of replacing a fuse should not be undertaken unless personnel have been taught how it should be done, the type of fuse that should be used and have been made aware of the dangers.

It may seem unreasonable that an entire office is put out of action whilst an electrician is sent for to replace a fuse, but the question that must arise is why did the fuse blow? If the answer is not immediately evident, such as the fuse blew at the same time as a tungsten lamp failed, technical knowledge is required to trace the reason; knowledge the manager is unlikely to have.

Where a company does not employ an electrical engineer, or competent electrical staff, they must go outside their organisation and employ a company which is competent to test and maintain their system. To reduce the time the office is brought to a standstill, managers can be trained in how to correctly install plug tops on leads and ensure the correct size and type of fuse is fitted. Should a piece of electrical equipment stop working, the manager can then check the plug and fuse, but if the equipment still does not work then outside expert help is needed.

All staff should be shown the correct way of inserting and withdrawing a plug. This is particularly pertinent with departmental stores and shops, where the function of electrical equipment is demonstrated to customers.

People have been seen inserting a plug with their fingers wrapped round the plug and almost touching the pins. The latest standards on plugs require part of the pins to be insulated and will go a long way to stopping this, but there will still be millions of the older type of plug still in use.

The installation of switched socket outlets, when properly used, will help in ensuring the safety of staff. The rule is switch off before inserting or removing a plug.

Electrical engineers

For those companies who do employ an electrical engineer, most of the following duties are going to fall on his shoulders and he will be responsible for:

- Producing the code of safe working practice for electrical personnel.
- Producing the code of safe working practice for non-electrical personnel working near live electrical equipment.
- Grading staff according to their competence.
- Ensuring staff are trained for the duties they have to perform.
- Ensuring staff are adequately supervised.
- Production of a maintenance, inspection and testing programme and maintaining the system so that it will not cause danger.
- Ensuring the electrical equipment has adequate strength and capability.

- Ensuring electrical equipment is suitable for the adverse or hazardous environments in which it is likely to be used.

- Ensuring that there is adequate working space, access and lighting at all electrical equipment on or near which work has to be done in circumstances that may give rise to danger.

- Ensuring that the necessary information concerning the system, its dangers and codes of practice are freely and readily available for the employees.

- Supervising subcontractors.

Subcontractors

Where subcontractors are working on your premises, or premises under your control, you are responsible for ensuring they are not injured whilst working on or near your electrical system. Apart from your duties under the HSW Act for their safety, you must also comply with Regulation 10 of the Management of Health and Safety at Work Regulations (MHSWR).

Regulation 12 (MHSWR): Persons working in host employers' or self-employed persons' undertakings

(1) Every employer and every self-employed person shall ensure that the employer of any employees from an outside undertaking who are working in his undertaking is provided with comprehensible information on -

(a) the risks to those employees' health and safety arising out of or in connection with the conduct by that first-mentioned employer or by that self-employed person of his undertaking; and

(b) the measures taken by that first-mentioned employer or by that self-employed person in compliance with the requirements and prohibitions imposed upon him by or under the relevant statutory provisions insofar as the said requirements and prohibitions relate to those employees.

(2) Paragraph (1) shall apply to a self-employed person who is working in the undertaking of an employer or a self-employed person as it applies to employees from an outside undertaking who are working therein; and the reference in that paragraph to the employer of any employees from an outside undertaking who are working in the undertaking of an employer or a self-employed person and the references in the said paragraph to employees from an outside undertaking who are working in the undertaking of an employer or a self-employed person shall be construed accordingly.

(3) Every employer shall ensure .... etc.

This regulation, which covers a full A4 page, requires every employer or self-employed person to ensure that the subcontract employer and any of his employees are provided with comprehensive information on the risks to those employees' health and safety arising from the working in his establishment. Additionally, the employer (or self-employed person) must ensure that any person who works for an outside company in his undertaking is provided with sufficient information to enable them to identify any person that the employer (or self-employed person) has nominated for the procedures for 'serious and imminent danger and for danger areas' as detailed by Regulation 8 of the MHSW Regulations.

If you provide an electrical service for the subcontractors' use, you are responsible for ensuring that there are no defects in that supply. The only sensible way of dealing with subcontractors is to have a code of safe working practice, coupled with a specification and certification arrangement for tools used.

Some companies insist that all tools brought onto the site must be tested and proved safe by their test department. This places the responsibility for those tools with the company and they would then be responsible for ensuring the tools are regularly maintained. The other way is for the subcontractor to provide certificates proving that they have been tested and maintained and comply with the EAW Regulations. Other items that the contractor can be made responsible for, although this will not negate the employer's responsibility, include:

- That each employee is given a copy of the company's code of safe working practice.
- The safe working conditions of his employees.
- Compliance with all current legislation including the HSW Act and the Electricity at Work Regulations.
- Ensuring that his employees have been made aware of their duties under the HSW Act, Electricity at Work Regulations and other current legislation.
- Ensuring that all electrical supplies are safe before use.
- That supplies for portable tools are protected by a residual current device, or that the voltage of all portable electrical tools must not exceed 110 volts and are fed through an isolation transformer manufactured to BS 3535 which gives 55 V to earth. Alternatively, that 110 V double insulated tools are used.
- Ensuring that all portable tools and extension leads have been tested and certified safe before bringing them onto site and each item is labelled, not to be used after ....month, ...year.
- That all electrical equipment used is regularly maintained and that portable equipment is inspected for damage before being used.
- That his employees are instructed as to the area in which they are allowed, all other areas being out of bounds.
- That his employees are instructed as to the entry and exit routes from the working area, both for normal use and in an emergency.

PERMIT - TO - WORK

N° ....

1. ISSUE

To ....

I hereby declare that it is safe to work on the following equipment, which is dead, isolated from all live conductors and is connected to earth :-

....

....

ALL OTHER APPARATUS IS DANGEROUS

Points at which the system is isolated ....

....

....

Caution notices are posted at ....

....

The apparatus is efficiently connected to earth at the following points:-

....

....

Other Precautions to be taken ....

....

The following work is to be carried out ....

....

Signed ....

being a Senior Authorised Person

Time .... Date ....

2. RECEIPT

I hereby declare that I accept responsibility for carrying out the work on the apparatus detailed on the Permit - to - Work and that no attempt will be made by me, or the men under my control, to carry out work on any other apparatus.

Signed ....

Time .... Date ....

Note: After signature for the work to proceed this Receipt must be signed by and the Permit - to - Work be retained by the person in charge of the work until the work is suspended or completed and the Clearance section has been signed.

3. CLEARANCE

I hereby declare that the work for which this Permit - to - Work was issued is now *suspended/completed, and that all men under my charge have been withdrawn and warned that it is no longer safe to work on the apparatus specified on this Permit - to - Work, and that gear, tools and additional earthing connections are all clear.

Signed ....

Time .... Date ....

*Delete word not applicable

4. CANCELLATION

This Permit - to - Work is hereby cancelled.

Signed ....

being a Senior Authorised person with authority to cancel a Permit-to-work

Figure 15.1 - Permit - to - Work

- Ensuring that all workers are competent for the work they are to do and that they are supervised by a person competent in the work to be undertaken.
- That his employees are fully aware of the company's safety policy.

There is a further duty on the occupier of the premises, and that is to ensure that the contractor's staff are made aware of what to do in the case of a fire alarm and know the safe routes out of the premises. In this respect the contractor's men should register with the company when they arrive on site, so that should a fire occur it is possible to know whether any person is left in the building. This, however, is more of a duty under the HSW Act than the Electricity at Work Regulations.

Permits to work

Although the Regulations do not specify that a permit to work is required where high voltage equipment is concerned or the system is complex and by the nature of the process live working has to be carried out, a permit to work system is essential to ensure the safety of workers. Such a permit can only be issued by a person who is competent at knowing what dangers can arise, knows what work has to be done, what is required to make the work area safe and knows the competence of the person who will carry out the work. He will also know whether that person needs to be accompanied in the interests of safety. Under the old Regulations such a person would have been an Authorised Person.

A permit to work system is laid down in BS 6626 :1985 the outline of which is given in Figure 16.1. BS 6626 also gives guidance on the maintenance of electrical switchgear and controlgear for voltages between 650 V and 36 kV. Although Figure 15.1 is designed for high voltage working, it can be modified to cater for other types of live working, including instructions on what should be done before live working is undertaken.

Hired electrical equipment

The question often arises as to who is responsible for hired electrical equipment. The hire tool firm is responsible for ensuring that all tools have been maintained and are safe before they are supplied to a customer. They will also be responsible for the electrical equipment being maintained to a regular programme. This is best achieved by carrying out a full inspection and test when the tool is returned and inspecting it before the tool it is reissued to another customer.

Once the customer is in possession of the electrical equipment he is responsible for ensuring that it is used properly. The customer is also responsible for ensuring that personnel using the equipment are competent to use such equipment and any equipment is taken out of service if it has become damaged.

Where the equipment is on hire for a long period, arrangements should be made with the hire firm to maintain the equipment at regular intervals or, providing the company has staff who are competent to maintain such equipment, arrange for the maintenance to be done by the company with agreement from the hire company. In these circumstances the company would be responsible for the electrical equipment as if they had purchased it.

Purchase / lease of equipment

Sometimes equipment is leased on the basis that at the end of the lease the equipment becomes the property of the company leasing the equipment. In these circumstances the company is responsible for the equipment as though they had purchased it outright. The limit of responsibility as far as the lessor is concerned is to ensure that the equipment, as supplied, is safe and complies with the Electricity at Work Regulations; a requirement that already exists under Section 6 of the HSW Act.

Chapter 17

Code of safe working practice

Throughout the handbook it has been mentioned that a code of safe working practice is required. This chapter is to give some guidance to those who have not had to draw up such a code in the past. It does not attempt to include all items that should be included in such a code, since this will depend upon the type of industry and the size of company involved. It is provided as an aide to compiling your own code of practice.

The number of codes required will depend upon whether the company is a purely commercial company or whether it is involved in manufacturing. To enable the reader to permutate his requirements depending upon the type of business they undertake, the requirements for each type of code will be discussed separately.

For those companies that manufacture or assemble a product and employ office staff and electrical and mechanical maintenance staff, three codes are required. These can, however, be incorporated into one code depending upon the size of the organisation.

Beginning of each code

The beginning of each code will be identical, by specifying that all existing personnel will be given a copy of the code, as well as any person joining the company. It will then go on to state the duties that are imposed on all employees by the Health and Safety at Work etc. Act, the Electricity at Work Regulations and the Management of Health and safety at work regulations. This could be followed by repeating Section 7 of the HSW Act, Regulation 3 of the Electricity at Work Regulations and Regulation 12 of the Management of Health and Safety at Work Regulations. Since Regulation 3 of the Electricity at Work Regulations spells out the duties of employers, Section 2 (1) and (2) of the HSW Act which stipulates the duties imposed on employers could also be included.

Employees should then be advised that these Acts are available for further reference, stating where they are kept and who they ask to enable the employee to read them. In large organisations copies of the Acts can be placed in each department or on notice boards.

The code would include an instruction that all accidents or dangerous occurrences must be reported to the person who has the job of recording such events and reporting them to the Health and Safety Executive.

Code of practice for office staff

For those commercial companies that employ only office staff, just a simple code is required. This could state that no employee must under any circumstances remove permanently fixed covers from electrical equipment. This could then be elaborated by listing equipment such as, electric typewriters, desk top computers, word processors, photocopiers etc.

The code can then instruct the staff that they must immediately report any equipment where the lead into the equipment has become damaged by for example: due to crushing (by for instance being trapped under a heavy desk leg); or where the leads have become slashed or the outer covering has split. Similarly they can be instructed to report any equipment where the lead into the plug or the equipment itself has become loose, exposing the inner cores of the cable.

The code can then go on to inform staff that no employee is allowed to bring on to the premises any personal electrical equipment for whatever reason. In those organisations which have an electrical maintenance department, the bringing of personal equipment onto the premises can be banned, unless prior permission has been obtained in writing. Permission only being given if any such equipment brought onto the premises has a certificate that it is safe from the electrical inspection department, who would label the equipment with the date when it has to be inspected and tested again.

The company should have had all the electrical equipment inspected and tested by a competent person or maintenance organisation and the equipment should therefore be labelled with a 'not to use after date'. The code can then instruct staff not to use equipment after the date stated on the equipment label.

A commercial company which does not employ electrical maintenance staff, or which has not trained its own staff to undertake inspection and testing, should contract with a maintenance company to regularly check their electrical equipment and installation. It will be the manager's duty to ensure that the electrical equipment is inspected before the expiry date on the equipment.

The company ought to ensure that the manager and at least one other person has received proper instruction on the fitting of plugs and the replacement of fuses in plugs. The code could then go on to state that any failure of the power supply to equipment is reported to the manager, who will then check the plug and replace the fuse in the plug if necessary.

Where such action does not restore the supply the code should instruct the selected maintenance firm to be called in to find the fault and rectify same.

Code of practice for mechanical fitters

For those companies employing fitters, the code of practice will depend to a large extent, on the amount of training they have received in switching off equipment driven by electrical means or to which an electrical supply is connected. In any event, it must specify that no work is to be carried out on equipment, unless all the electrical supplies to the equipment have been disconnected. This also means that in compliance with EAW Regulation 12 and PUWER Regulations 23 and 24 the means of disconnecting the supply to the equipment will have been suitably identified, so that there can be no confusion or mistakes made.

Where isolators are used, the code must also instruct that the load is switched off before isolators are operated. To comply with EAW Regulation 13, it can then instruct that the fitter's personal padlock is fitted to the isolator, so that it cannot be switched on by anyone else.

Since equipment cannot be assumed to be dead by the mere operation of an isolator or switch, the mechanical fitter should have received training using a simple instrument in checking that the equipment is dead and the procedure to be used. The next instruction would then be for the fitter to test to ensure that the equipment is dead before proceeding, and check the test instrument before and after use. The code should also list the procedures that have to be adopted in restoring the supply to the equipment.

Where no training has been given to mechanical fitters the code will instruct that no work is to be carried out until the equipment has been isolated and proved dead by the electrical staff. At this point the electrician as well as the fitter would then insert their padlocks in the isolator again in compliance with EAW Regulation 13.

The code would also instruct fitters to install a jump-lead across any pipes, before they carry out an alteration to the pipe work. The code would also detail precautions to be taken when welding is being performed using portable electrical tools and the precautions to be taken when using such tools outside the building.

The code would detail the procedures for working near overhead cranes, or external overhead lines, or for carrying out excavation work, and specify that ladders or long objects shall be carried parallel to the ground.

It should also give details of what to do when a person is receiving an electric shock as detailed in the code for electrical staff.

The code could then continue with the normal safety requirements for mechanical fitters when working on or using compressed air, or working on steam mains etc.

Code of practice for electrical staff

The electrical code of safe working practice should contain clauses on, making certain there was adequate access, working space and lighting at electrical equipment on which work was to be carried out to comply with Regulation 15. It should cover such items as the availability of fire extinguishing equipment being available that was suitable for use on live electrical equipment.

Instructions should be included in the code for employees to acquaint themselves with the procedures to adopt if a person is receiving an electric shock. The code should contain a section detailing the actions to be taken with photographs illustrating how to carry out artificial respiration.

· The code should include instructions to the effect that no work is to be carried out live, unless a permit to work live has been obtained and should then detail the procedures to be adopted.

Instructions that no person is to perform any of the following actions unless he has been instructed to do so should be included in the code.

1. Enter a substation, open link boxes, climb overhead line pole or tower, or touch the insulation covering or supporting any conductor, or interfere with any item of plant.

2. Commence work until he fully understands the instructions he has received and not to exceed the limit of those instructions.

3. Interfere with earth connections, locks, danger notices, testing-in-progress notices, safety barriers, lamps or flags or other safety devices.

4. Ladders or long objects shall be carried parallel to the ground and not be taken into substations.

5. The employees attention should be drawn to Regulation 14 of the Management of Health and Safety at Work Regulations, which requires an employee to inform his employer of any shortcoming in the employer's protection arrangements for health and safety. The employee is also required to inform his employer, and any employee responsible for health and safety, of any work situation which he considers represents a serious and immediate danger to health and safety. This effectively reinforces Section 7 of the HSW Act.

Instructions on the use of portable electric tools should be included, stating the maximum voltage to earth allowed with such tools and that where they are used outside, the supply must be obtained through an RCD.

The safety policy to be adopted should be listed where live working has to be carried out, this would include sample forms of the permits to work and guide lines on how the permit to work system works. Details of the procedures to be taken concerning the screening of all earthed metalwork and live parts should be given, with instructions that these should all be in place before any live working is commenced.

Depending upon the voltage to be worked on, the code can also specify that rubber gloves and mats are to be used. Where rubber gloves are used the code should give the rules for the storing, issuing and inspection of gloves as detailed in BS 697.

Extracts from BS 6423 'Maintenance of electrical switchgear and controlgear for voltages up to 1000 Volt' can be included in the code. The precautions to be taken when inspecting and testing the installation, including reference to any Health and Safety Executive Codes of practice which are applicable to the type of equipment in use, can also be included in the code. The code will also specify that no instrument is to be used without fusible leads.

The code can also detail the rules that have to be complied with when new work, or an alteration, or an extension to an existing installation, is carried out. It can start by specifying that all electrical installation work shall be carried out in accordance with the latest edition of the IEE Wiring Regulations BS7671 and where hazardous areas are involved can specify the applicable British Standards that have to be complied with, such as BS 5501 BS EN 50014, BS EN 5028 and BS EN 6007.

Where high voltage is involved, the permit to work system is essential and the code should cover the procedures, including who is responsible for issuing such a permit and detailing who is, and who is not allowed, to operate or work on high voltage equipment. It can elaborate on the maintenance to be carried out by using extracts from BS 6626.

Identifying work functions

Producing a Code of Safe Working Practice is best done by identifying each work function and listing the dangers and the items that can cause danger if someone does something wrong. The code can then be written to outline the methods of working that will avoid such dangers.

The code can be modified in the light of experience, but a written code is essential, since it is impossible to rely on memory in carrying out a work activity. Above all, it must be seen that the company has done everything it possibly could to comply with current legislation.

Final warning

The Electricity at Work Regulations impose duties which are enforceable in the criminal courts. Should there be a dangerous occurrence or an accident, the duty holders could find themselves being prosecuted under the HSW Act and where a breach of statutory duty is proved, they could also find themselves involved in a civil action for damages.

Make no mistake, the attitude to electrical safety has changed, the likelihood of a prosecution now is greater than it has been in the past, especially if the dangerous occurrence or accident occurred in breach of EAW Regulation 14.

Appendix A

Standards

The amount of information required when designing or maintaining an installation will vary with the type of installation involved. The following list has been compiled to assist in the location of additional information. Where possible a synopsis of the contents has been included to give the reader some idea as to how useful the publication may be.

IEC Standards

60479-1 Part 1   **Third Edition - Effects of current on human beings** - General aspects; gives characteristics of the impedance of the human body; initial and total impedance; effects of direct and alternating current.

60479-2   **Effects of current passing through the human body** - Special aspects; effects of special waveforms; impulse currents.

60479-3   **Effects of current passing through the body of livestock.**

501   **Safety requirements for arc welding equipment - Plugs; socket outlets and couplers for welding cables.** - construction; rating; temperature rise test; protection against electric shock; climatic tests; cable fixing test; crush test; marking.

60519-1 Part 1   **Safety in electroheat installations. General requirements.** - Gives classification of equipment according to voltage and frequency; protection against overcurrent, electric shock, thermal influences; risk of fire, danger and explosion; isolation and switching; prohibition of using earth as part of active circuit.

60519-2 Part 2   **Particular requirements for resistance heating equipment.**

60519-3 Part 3   **Particular requirements for induction and conduction heating and induction melting installations.**

60519-4 Part 4   **Particular requirements for arc furnace installations.**

60519-5/8 Parts 5/8 **Covers other forms of heating and melting processes.**

60519-9 Part 9   **Particular requirements for high-frequency dielectric heating installations.**

724	**Guide to the short-circuit temperature limits of electric cables with a rated voltage not exceeding 0.6 / 1.0 kV.** - Gives guidance on the design of accessories; influences on the method of installation; calculation of permissible short-circuit currents; factors governing the application of temperature limits.
781	**Application guide for calculation of short-circuit currents in low-voltage radial systems.** - Gives calculation methods and calculation assumptions; symmetrical components; equivalent voltage at short-circuit location; conditions for disregarding the influence of motors; example calculations, includes example of distribution system calculation to a housing estate; mainly for overhead lines but contains useful information.
BS EN 60950	**Safety of information technology equipment including business equipment.** - Includes safe electrical design; wiring and connections; construction; thermal and electrical tests.
Guide 105	**Principles concerning the safety of equipment electrically connected to telecommunications network.** - Covers operating Voltages; protection of consumer from Voltages on lines and equipment; test procedures.

British Standards

BS 697	**Rubber gloves for electrical purposes**. - Gives requirements for all gloves up to 4000 V ; Guidance on storage; issue; examination before use; precautions in use; inspection and re-testing; dimensions.
BS 921	**Rubber mats for electrical purposes**. - Gives composition; thickness; width; workmanship and finish of rubber mats along with electrical and compression tests. No information on maintenance.
BS 2754	**Construction of electrical equipment for protection against electric shock**. - Forms of construction and classification; design requirements; tests; marking of equipment; methods of achieving double insulation.
BS 2771	**Part 1 Electrical equipment of industrial machines.** - Gives details of warning signs; protection against electric shock; control and signalling circuits; cables and conductors; wiring; electric motors; connection to accessories and local lighting; current-carrying capacities of conductors. No information given on maintenance.

BS 4363	**Distribution assemblies for electricity supplies for construction and building sites.** - Gives the service conditions; mechanical design; minimum space requirements; input and outputs allowed, with a schematic layout of units.
BS 4444	**Guide to electrical earth monitoring and protective conductor proving**. - Gives principle, advantages, design, practical arrangements; pilot core protection; siting of monitoring units; earth leakage protection; checking the operation of units.
BS 5266	**Part 1 Code of practice for the emergency lighting of premises other than cinemas and other certain specified premises used for entertainment.** - Gives recommendations for providing adequate illumination; the illumination of fire alarm points and fire fighting equipment. (see also BS EN 1838)
BS 5372	**Specification for dimensions of cable terminations for 3 and 4 core polymetric insulated cables rated at 660/1000 V and 1900/3300 V having aluminium conductors.** - Gives details of space to allow at terminations for lugs and spreading of cores.
BS 5501	**Electrical apparatus for potentially explosive atmospheres.** - Gives requirements for all electrical apparatus; supplementary requirements for certain electrical apparatus; verification and tests; marking; Parts 1 to 9.
BS 5655	**Safety rules for the construction and installation of electric lifts** - Gives details of the construction and equipment of machine rooms specifying the width, height, and depth to be allowed in front of control panels; specifies minimum size required for access doors into machine room.
BS 5839	**Part 1 Fire detection and alarm systems for buildings, Code of practice for system design, installation and servicing.** - Covers all systems, from simple manual installations with several manual call points to complex automatic installations with manual call points; detectors; connection to fire service and initiation of ancillary services.
BS 5958	**Part 1 Control of undesirable static electricity - general considerations.** - Gives fundamentals of static electricity; electrostatic hazards and their control; earthing and bonding; guidance on methods of measuring/estimating various parameters; various tables including summary of recommended earthing resistance for the control of static electricity.
BS 5958	**Part 2 Control of undesirable static electricity - particular**

industrial situations. - Gives recommendations for particular industrial situations; fixed and unfixed tanks for the storage of liquids, transferring liquid from road/rail tankers; small metallic/nonmetallic containers for liquids; tank cleaning with high pressure water jets; aircraft fuelling; metal containers with inside or outside nonmetallic covering; pipelines for liquids and gases; release of gasses and vapours; spraying of paints and powders; rigid plastics sheeting, walls and screens; earthing of personnel; hazards from clothing.

BS 6423   **Maintenance of electrical switchgear and controlgear up to 1 kV.**- Covers safety; common recommendations relating to maintenance; additional recommendations for specific items including busbars, circuit breakers, fuses, timing devices liquid starters and controllers etc.; guidelines on safe isolation procedures; example of maintenance record chart; maintenance; operation of circuit breakers.

BS 6467   **Electrical apparatus with protection by enclosure for use in the presence of combustible dusts.** - Gives details of the requirements based on maximum surface temperature of the enclosure and on the restriction of dust ingress to the enclosure.

BS 6467   **Part 2 Ditto. Guide to selection, installation and maintenance.** - Complies with Part 1, based on the legal requirements in the U.K. for minimising the release of dust and preventing the formation of dust layers.

BS 6626   **Maintenance of electrical switchgear and controlgear for Voltages between 1 kV and 36 kV.** - Has a section on safety; common recommendations relating to maintenance; additional recommendations for specific items; gives list of maintenance operations for circuit breakers; gives Electricity Board Safety Rules (Distribution); model forms for Permits to Work, testing and access.

BS 6651   **Code of Practice for protection of structures against lightning.** - Gives details of bonding to services within the building via the main earth bar; details of design; inspection and testing; maintenance refers you to the testing section.

BS 6742   **Part 1 Specification for hand-held spray guns and associated apparatus.** - Gives constructional and test requirements for spray guns and associated apparatus used to spray flammable paints, powders, or flocks; including spraying flocks on to adhesives which may form a potentially explosive atmosphere.

BS 6742   **Part 2 Specification for selection, installation and use of hand held spray guns (energy limit of 0.24 mJ) and associated apparatus.** - Gives requirements for spray guns and associated apparatus complying with Part 1.

BS 6907   **Part 1 Electrical installations for opencast mines and quarries. Glossary.** - Only contains definitions.

BS 6907   **Part 2 Ditto. General recommendations for protection against direct contact and electric shock.** - Repeats information from the IEE Wiring Regulations; gives information on minimum sizes for aerial and suspended protective conductors; has a section on protection against overcurrent and fault currents and an appendix covering the selection of 'k' factor for protective conductors.

BS 6907   **Part 3 Ditto. Recommendations for equipment and ancillaries.** - Gives recommendations on rotating machines, transformers, static converters, switching devices, cable selection and application; cable connectors; cable drums; control circuits and control devices; safety circuits and safety devices; fire detection and protection systems.

BS 6907   **Part 4 Ditto. Recommendations for winding, stacking and processing machinery, pumps and low signals level and communications systems** - Gives guidance on principles for installation and operation of electrical equipment to ensure safety of persons, livestock, property and the proper functioning of the plant.

BS 6907   **Part 5 Ditto Recommendations for operation**. - Gives guidance on principles for installation and operation of electrical equipment to ensure safety of persons, livestock, property and the proper functioning of the plant.

BS 7375   **Code of practice for distribution of electricity on construction and building sites.** - Low voltage installations; recommendations for testing and maintenance; covers electricity supplies and distribution systems.

BS 7430   **Code of practice for Earthing.** - Supply system earthing, electrical equipment earthing; earthing methods, soil resistivity, earthing cathodically protected structures, potential gradient round earth electrodes, periodic inspection and testing of earthing system; earthing applications, generating plant, consumers' electrical installations, temporary scaffolding, hazardous areas; supplies to caravan pitch.

BS 7671   **Requirements for electrical installations IEE Wiring Regulations. Sixteenth edition. -** Gives the requirements for electrical installations up to 1000V ; Fundamental requirements for safety; definitions; assessment of general characteristics; protection for safety; selection and erection of equipment; special installations; inspection and testing; characteristics of protective devices; current-carrying capacity of cables; Inspection and completion certificate; list of statutory regulations.

BS 8313   **Code of practice for accommodation of building services in ducts.** - Recommendations for design; construction; installation and maintenance.

CP 1007   **Maintained lighting for cinemas** - Relates to the safety lighting and management lighting in various parts.

BS EN 1838   **Lighting applications.** Emergency lighting.

BS EN 50014   **Electrical apparatus for potentially explosive atmospheres.** General requirements.

BS EN 50281   **Electrical apparatus for use in the presence of combustible dust.**

BS EN 60079   **Electrical apparatus for potentially explosive gas atmospheres.**

BS EN 60079-10   **Classification of hazardous areas.**

BS EN 60079-14   **Electrical installations in hazardous areas (other than mines).**

BS EN 60079-17   **Inspection and maintenance of electrical installations in hazardous areas (other than mines).**

BS EN 60129   **Specification for alternating current disconnectors and earthing switches.**

BS EN 60298   **AC metal - enclosed switchgear and controlgear for rated voltages above 1kV and up to and including 52kV.**

BS EN 60439   **Specification for low-voltage switchgear and controlgear assemblies.** - Gives electrical characteristics for the assembly; specifies manufacturers should give instructions for installation, operation and maintenance; marking of assembly; service conditions; design and construction; test specifications. No installation, or maintenance information included. Referred to by BS EN 60439-1.

BS EN 60439-3   **Particular requirements for low-voltage switchgear and controlgear assemblies intended to be installed in places**

where unskilled persons have access to their use.

Distribution boards. Supplementary requirements to IEC 439-1 for enclosed distribution boards for indoor use, intended for use in domestic applications or other applications where unskilled persons have access to their use.

BS EN 60529 **Specification for degrees of protection provided by enclosures (IP code).** - Gives degrees of protection by the enclosure against persons and solid foreign bodies and ingress of liquids; marking; tests on enclosure; gives details of supplementary markings A, B, C & D which specifies that equipment has additional protection, supplementary markings giving additional information on whether protection provided whilst equipment is stationary or moving.

BS EN 60898 **Specification for circuit breakers for overcurrent protection for household and similar installations.** - For voltages up to 440 V, current up to 125 A and prospective current up to 25 kA.

BS EN 60947-1 **Specification for low-voltage switchgear and control gear (general rules).** - This part is used in conjunction with all other parts in the series; defines all rules and requirements of a general nature.

BS EN 60947-2 **Circuit breakers.** - Characteristics, conditions for operation, marking requirements for CBs used in circuits up to 1000 V a.c; additional requirements for integrally fused circuit breakers; gives the tests for ultimate breaking capacity I_{cu} and the service rating breaking capacity I_{cs}.

BS EN 60947-3 **Switches, disconnectors, switch-disconnectors and fuse combination units.** - Characteristics, conditions of use and tests for items used in distribution circuits and motor circuits up to 1000 V a.c; information on equipment marking.

BS EN 60947-4-1 **Electromechanical contactors and motor starters** for Voltages up to 1000 V. - Requirements for contactors associated with overload and/or short-circuit protective devices; starters with separate short-circuit protective devices or with separate or integrated overload protective devices.

BS EN 60947-5 **Control circuit devices and switching elements.**

BS EN 60947-6 **Specification for low-voltage switchgear and controlgear. Multiple function equipment.**

BS EN 60950   **Specification for safety of information technology equipment, including electrical business equipment.** - Intended to prevent injury from electric shock, energy, fire, mechanical, heat, radiation and chemical hazards related to the office environment.

IEC Standards and British Standards are obtainable from BSI, Linford Wood, Milton Keynes, MK14 6LE. Tel: 0908 221166.

BS 7671 is also available from the Institution of Electrical Engineers, Savoy Place, London WC2R 0BL. Tel: 071 2401871

Appendix B

Additional information

Health & Safety Executive Guides

GS 6 1991   **Avoidance of danger from overhead electric lines.** - Working near overhead lines; precautions to be taken, working near lines, passing under lines, working beneath lines.

GS 7 1989   **Accidents to children on construction sites**. - General precautions; specific precautions; exclusion of children by fencing; precautions where fencing not possible; gives one paragraph on electrical precautions.

GS 23 1990   **Electrical safety in schools (Electricity at Work Regulations 1989).** - Electrical installations; apparatus; science laboratories and other practical areas; live working .

GS 27 1984   **Protection against electric shock.** - Details the danger; prevention; reduced voltage; extra low voltage; enclosure of apparatus; earthing and automatic disconnection of the supply; residual current devices; limitation of energy; separation of supplies; portable equipment; maintenance; connection of electricity systems.

GS 34 1986   **Electrical safety in departments of electrical engineering.** - Precautions to be taken.

GS 38 1991   **Electrical test equipment for use by electricians.** - The dangers; the causes; safety requirements; systems of work.

GS 43 1987   **Lithium batteries.** - Dangers; testing by manufacturers/ suppliers; protective devices; information to be supplied; selection and design; using lithium batteries; testing by purchaser/user; accident procedure; transportation and disposal; safety measures; dangerous incidents with batteries.

GS 47 1991   **Safety of electrical distribution systems on factory premises.** Gives some of the problems found in high voltage and low voltage installations; gives details of dangers that have been found; still uses term medium voltage instead of low-voltage

GS 50 1991   **Electrical safety at places of entertainment -** Results of a survey by the Field Consultant Group electrical inspectors of some 80 premises.

HS (G) 38 1987   **Lighting at work.** - How lighting affects health and safety; lighting recommendations; lighting equipment; lighting installations; emergency lighting.

HS (G) 47 1989   **Avoiding dangers from underground services** - The dangers; safe systems of work; safe systems of work for trenchless methods; new housing developments; installation of new services near existing services; demolition sites.

HS (G) 85 2001   **Electricity at work: safe working practices -** Gives guidance on the essential elements that need to be considered when devising safe working practices for people to carry out work on or near electrical equipment in circumstances in which danger may arise.

HS (G) 107 1994   **Maintaining portable and transportable electrical equipment -** Covers duties under the law; controlling the risk; use of equipment; construction of equipment; environment; maintenance.

HS (G) 150 (rev)   **Health and Safety in construction**

     - HSE Your guide to the essentials of electrical safety.

     - HSE Avoiding danger from underground services.

PM 29 1988   **Electrical hazards from steam/water pressure cleaners etc.** - Accidents; design considerations; installation precautions; use and maintenance.

PM 32 1990   **The safe use of portable electrical apparatus.** - Accidents; methods of minimising the risk of electric shock; precautions; small portable & mobile generators; larger mobile plant; inspection and maintenance; operator safety.

PM 38 1992   **Selection and use of electric handlamps.** - Electric shock; selection of handlamps to prevent electric shock; fire and explosion; selection of handlamps for use in potentially explosive atmospheres; use of; inspection and maintenance.

PM 41 1984   **The application of photoelectric safety systems to machinery.** - Factors affecting the suitability of an installation; alternative formats for photoelectric curtains; classification of machinery; installation; examination inspection and test.

PM 53 1985   **Emergency private generation: electrical safety.** - General safety considerations; electrical safety principles; transfer switching equipment; protection of live conductors; means of cutting off the supplies and for safe isolation; connections, cables and components; electrical protection; bonding and earthing; emergency load operation.

PM 64 1986   **Electrical safety in arc welding.** - Processes and equipment; the welding circuit; electrical hazards; precautions; fire precautions; information and training; inspection and maintenance.

Safe use of electrical induction furnaces.
Limited amount of information included concerning electrical work.

The protection of persons against ionising radiation arising from any work activity (Approved code) 1987.
Approved code based on The Ionising Radiations Regulations 1985.

Memorandum of guidance on the Electricity at Work Regulations 1989.
Gives a brief outline of the regulations, but excludes those for mines.

The use of electricity at quarries Electricity at Work Regulations 1989 (Approved code) 1989.
Gives a brief outline of the regulations as applied to quarries.

The use of electricity in mines Electricity at Work Regulations 1989 (Approved code) 1989.
Gives a brief outline of the regulations as applied to mines.

A guide to the HSW Act 1990.
A general explanation of those parts of the HSW Act applicable to employers and employees.

Management of Health and Safety at Work Regulations 1999 - (Approved code) Guidance on the regulations 1992.

Provision and Use of work Equipment Regulations 1998 (PUWER) - Guidance on the regulations. 1992

Workplace (Health, Safety and Welfare Regulations 1992 - (Approved code) (WHSWR) guidance on the regulations 1992.

Personal Protective Equipment at Work Regulations 1992 (PPEWR) - guidance on the regulations.

HSE Guides and the above publications are issued by the Health and Safety Executive available from HSE Books, PO Box 1999 Sudbury Suffolk CO10 6FS. Tel: 0787 881165.

Useful books etc.

Electric Fuses by A. Wright & P. G. Newbery.
Covers the pre-arcing behaviour; the arcing behaviour; the construction and types of low-voltage fuses; protection of cables and motors and the application of fuses. Published by Peter Peregrinus Ltd.

Touch Voltages in Electrical Installations by B. D. Jenkins
A technical treatise providing a comprehensive introduction to the touch voltage conception leading to a fuller understanding of the requirements for earthed equipotential bonding and automatic disconnection of the supply. Published by Blackwell Scientific Publications.

Electrical Safety Engineering by W. Fordham Cooper.
A highly technical book for electrical engineers on electrical safety. Published by Butterworths.

The Commissioning of Electrical Plant by R. C. H. Richardson.
Covers commissioning alternators, motors, transformers; parallel operation of transformers; transformer troubles; direct current generators, motors, rotary converters, rectifiers; commissioning of circuit breakers.
Although last revised and published in 1962 by Chapman and Hall it is still worth reading (probably only available from a library).

Handbook on the IEE Wiring Regulations Revised Sixth Edition by Trevor E. Marks.
The book contains four parts, Part 1 gives BS 7671 IEE Wiring Regulations under subject titles in a language which is easily understood. Part 2 explains the regulations with numerous worked examples and calculations with a chapter on inspection and testing. Part 3 gives installation tables making a large number of calculations unnecessary. Part 4 gives the necessary design data needed by engineers and technicians to design installations which is not available in BS 7671. ISBN 1-904126-02-2
Published by William Ernest Publishing Limited, Unit 6, Willow Court, Cordy Lane Underwood, Nottingham NG16 5FD Tel: 01773 764288, Fax: 01773 764282.

Electrical Distribution in Buildings by C. Dennis Poole Revised by Trevor E. Marks
Covers electrical supplies; private generation supplies; uninterruptible power

supplies; distribution systems and equipment; main and standby distribution; busbar distribution systems; cable types and applications; cable sizing; protective devices; cable support systems; enclosed wiring systems; final circuit design; special cabling requirements; computer control of environmental services; emergency lighting; earthing; lightning protection; fire precautions and protection; installation, inspection and testing.

Published by Blackwell obtainable from William Ernest Publishing Limited, Unit 6 Willow Court, Cordy Lane, Underwood Nottingham NG16 5FD Tel; 01773 764288. Fax: 01773 764282.

A Practical Guide to the Wiring Regulations by Geoffrey Stokes.
by Blackwell Science. ISBN 0-632-05898-6

EEA recommendations for periodic safety checks for business equipment - Gives details of the dangers of damaging computers etc., when testing to comply with the Electricity at Work Regulations; gives guidance on inspection and testing business equipment and the test Voltages and currents.

Published by EEA, Russell Square House, 10-12 Russell Square, London WC1B 5AE.

ECMA - European Computer Manuufacturers Association
Standard ECMA 97 - Local Area networks safety requirements.
Standard ECMA 129 Information technology equipment safety (two volumes).
ECMA - TR/63 - Alphabetical Reference index to IEC 950.
Published by ECMA 114 Rue du Rhône- CH 1204 Geneva Switzerland.

Addresses

Seton Ltd , PO Box 77, Banbury, Oxon OX16 7LS
Metrotest Instruments, Littleburn Ind. Estate, Langley Moor Durham DH7 8HJ
Avo International, Archcliffe Road, Dover Kent CT17 9EN

Appendix C

Resistance of cable leads

Table 1 - **Class 5 flexible copper conductors for single core and multicore cables. Resistance of plain copper conductors at 20°C BS6360: 1991 PVC insulated cores.**

Cable lead	Resistance in mΩ of protective conductor for cable size in mm²						
Length metres	0.5	0.75	1.0	1.25	1.5	2.5	4.0
1.0	39.0	26.0	19.5	15.6	13.3	7.98	4.95
2.0	78.0	52.0	39.0	31.2	26.60	15.96	9.90
3.0	117.0	78.0	58.5	46.8	39.90	23.94	14.85
4.0	156.0	104.0	78.0	62.4	53.20	31.92	19.80
5.0	195.0	130.0	97.5	78.0	66.50	39.90	24.75
6.0	234.0	156.0	117.0	93.6	79.80	47.88	29.70
7.0	273.0	182.0	136.5	109.2	93.10	55.86	34.65
8.0	312.0	208.0	156.0	124.8	106.40	63.84	39.60
9.0	351.0	234.0	175.5	140.4	119.70	71.82	44.55
10.0	390.0	260.0	195.0	156.0	133.00	79.80	49.50

Table 2 - **Class 5 flexible copper conductors for single core and multicore cables. Resistance of tinned copper conductors at 20°C BS6360: 1991 Rubber insulated cores.**

Cable lead	Resistance in mΩ of protective conductor for cable size in mm²						
Length metres	0.5	0.75	1.0	1.25	1.5	2.5	4.0
1.0	40.1	26.7	20.0	16.1	13.7	8.21	5.09
2.0	80	53	40	32.2	27.4	16.42	10.18
3.0	120	80	60	48.3	41.1	24.63	15.27
4.0	160	107	80	64.4	54.8	32.84	20.36
5.0	200	134	100	80.5	68.5	41.05	25.45
6.0	241	160	120	96.6	82.2	49.26	30.54
7.0	281	187	140	112.7	95.9	57.47	35.63
8.0	321	214	160	128.8	109.6	65.68	40.72
9.0	361	240	180	144.9	123.3	73.89	45.81
10.0	401	267	200	161.0	137.0	82.10	50.90

Note: A mΩ is one milliohm, divide by 1000 to get the resistance in ohms.
For IBM power cable leads the resistance measured should align with Table 1

Index

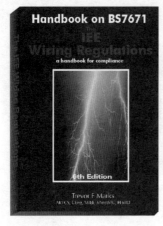

The Definitive Guide to BS 7671 (2001)

The IEE Wiring Regulations
by Trevor E. Marks

A Handbook for Compliance

An invaluable reference book for electricians and electrical plant designers. Provides in one handbook a summary on BS 7671 2001 (The IEE Wiring Regulations), a guide to their interpretation and application, and all the necessary installation tables. Fully typeset and divided into four parts, each printed on different coloured paper for ease of use reference.

Part 1   Gives the BS 7671 2001 (IEE Wiring Regulations) under subject titles in an easy to understand language. Each paragraph gives reference to the original regulation number.

Part 2   Explains the regulations in an order which illustrates how an installation should be designed. Subjects covered include, assessment, selecting protective devices, overloads, derating of conductors, voltage drop, shock protection, circuit protective conductors, fault currents, short circuit currents, isolation and switching, mechanical maintenance, emergency switching, inspection and testing.

Part 3   Gives Tables for maximum length circuits can be to comply with the Regulations including tables giving the maximum length of cable sizes required when grouped in different modes, values of earth loop impedance Zs for design and testing, maximum Zs for protective conductors, capacity of trunking and conduit etc.

Part 4   Over 40 tables giving the information necessary when designing installations, from the impedance of transformers to the impedance of conduit. Contains characteristics of mcbs rewirable fuses and HRC fuses.

An essential book for all electricians, electrical engineers and anybody needing to make sense of the IEE Wiring Regulations.

Price: £36.00 + p (ISBN 1 904126 02 2)

PRINTING FOR ELECTRICIANS

PHASE

- COMPLETION CERTIFICATES
- INSPECTION CERTIFICATES
- INSPECTION REPORTS
- INSPECTION LABELS

ALL YOU COULD POSSIBLY EVER NEED FROM THE ELECTRICIANS PRINTER.

- PHASE MARKETING
- PHASE DESIGN
- PHASE DIGITAL PRINT
- PHASE COLOUR PRINT
- PHASE STATIONERY PRINT

ALL UNDER ONE ROOF.

PHASE
WILLOW COURT
CORDY LANE
UNDERWOOD
NOTTINGHAMSHIRE
NG16 5FD
TEL: 01773 764288
FAX: 01773 764282
WEB: www.phaseprint.com
Email: sales@phaseprint.com

NOTES: